D0924789

Guide to the Identification
and Ageing of Holarctic Waders

Spoon-billed Sandpiper *Eurynorhynchus pygmeus* (above) and Lesser Sandplover *Charadrius mongolus stegmanni* (below) on nests in NE USSR.

Guide to the Identification and Ageing of Holarctic Waders

Tony Prater and John Marchant
B.T.O., Tring

and

Juhani Vuorinen
Norrköping, Sweden.

British Trust for Ornithology
Field Guide Seventeen

British Trust for Ornithology
Beech Grove, Tring, Herts.

First Published 1977

Printed by Maund & Irvine Ltd., Tring, Herts.

Contents

PREFACE

This guide has been produced with the help of many people. Their advice has been received most gratefully and their comments incorporated into the text. However, we must take full responsibility for the information given here. We also realise that much remains to be learned about wader populations, their moult strategies and the methods of ageing, sexing and identification. Therefore we will be extremely pleased to learn of any additional characters which are found to be of help. As these, and no doubt much additional biometric (including weight) data, will be forthcoming in the near future, it is expected that further editions of this guide will be needed to incorporate additions and corrections. Please send any information to the authors, c/o A. J. Prater, British Trust for Ornithology, Beech Grove, Tring, Hertfordshire HP23 5NR.

GUIDE TO THE IDENTIFICATION AND AGEING OF HOLARCTIC WADERS

INTRODUCTION

Considerable attention has been focussed recently on estuaries, coastlines and inland wetlands. They have become increasingly under threat from a multitude of development schemes and as a result many studies have been made of their bird populations. Waders from the nine families of the Order Charadriiformes form an important and, in many areas, a key group of species since most depend entirely on the wetlands.

In any study it is essential to identify accurately the species and to discern the age and sex patterns and racial structure of the populations involved. Fortunately only a relatively small number of species of waders from the bulk of the non-breeding concentrations seen throughout the world. Many species, especially from the arctic regions, undertake prodigious migrations which take them as far south as South Africa, Tierra del Fuego in South America, or New Zealand in Australasia. There is a need for international co-operation and standardisation in these studies. Many papers and handbooks have been published which include incidental remarks on the techniques involved and characters of use for ageing waders. However, apart from two preliminary accounts (Minton 1971, Robbins 1973), no synthesis of experience gained and data published has been attempted.

SCOPE OF GUIDE

This guide is aimed primarily at ringers who have the opportunity to examine waders in the hand. It is hoped that it will also be of considerable help to museum workers. It does, however, contain much information on identification and ageing, sexing and racial characters which, hopefully, birdwatchers will find of considerable help in the field.

The geographical area covered by the guide comprises the Palaearctic and Nearctic faunal regions. The order of species follows Voous (1973) and all species of the families Rostratulidae, Haematopodidae, Ibidorhynchidae, Recurvirostridae, Dromadidae, Burhinidae, Glareolidae, Charadriidae and Scolopacidae regularly breeding within the Holarctic are described in detail, with emphasis on the most numerous ones. In addition identification features of irregularly breeding or vagrant species are included. We differ from Voous's species list in upgrading the American Oystercatcher *Haematopus palliatus* and Black-necked Stilt *Himantopus mexicanus* to the species level, while regarding the Amami Woodcock *Scolopax mira* as conspecific with *S. rusticola*. It is hoped that these changes will make the accounts clearer.

About 58% of the world's wader species breed in the Holarctic and come within the scope of the guide. These include all the regular intercontinental migrants and form a high proportion of the waders found in any part of the world at the appropriate season.

The remaining species can perhaps be aged by application of the general methods of ageing waders described later in this introduction, but there will be additional problems because of accelerated feather wear in the tropics and irregular or unknown breeding seasons and moult periods.

SOURCES OF DATA

The data included in this guide come from many sources. Identification, ageing characters and moult patterns have all been checked or determined by AJP and JHM from the skin collection in the British Museum (Natural History) at Tring, and by JV at the Zoological Institute of the University of Helsinki and the Norrköpings Biologiska Forening. However, many of them originate from extensive field observations made by ringers in all parts of the world and their help in the production of this guide cannot be too highly stressed. Some data have been obtained from the collection at Berkeley, University of California, and detailed comments have been received from Liverpool Polytechnic, where several taxonomic studies are being made. The measurements are all obtained from museum collections but a sample of them have been compared with live birds measured by ringers in Britian. (See Figure 9).

The amount of data given for each species varies, depending mainly on the size of the collection available for study. The accounts of most (and all abundant) species are based on samples of at least one hundred birds, while ageing characters were checked on much larger samples. The drawbacks of using museum compared with live measurements are discussed later.

DETAILED USE OF GUIDE

Each species account is set out in a standard way — distribution and migration, identification, ageing, sexing, geographical variation and biometrics. Relevant references are listed at the end of each species text. We have not included references within each account but must emphasise that the text is partly a distillation of already published material.

a) **Area codes**

These form a quick notation of the breeding distributions. They do however involve some simplification and therefore only provide an indication of the likely occurrence of each species in any area. The symbols used are presented in Figure 1. The distance of migration also suggests the wintering distribution and the likelihood of the species occurring outside its usual range.

b) **Identification**

Only the principal features of the species are given, with emphasis on the bird in the hand. The most obvious field characters are included, although habits and calls are not discussed. Where difficult pairs of species are involved this section is enlarged.

14

Figure 1. Regions of the world referred to in distribution section.
H = Holarctic; N = Nearctic; P = Palaearctic; (N) = Neotropical;
(E) = Ethiopian; (O) = Oriental; (A) = Australasian;
N,M,S, = north, mid, south; W,C,E, = west, central,east.

c) **Ageing**   i) **Terminology**

Unfortunately several different ageing terminologies are used by ringing schemes and taxonomists. It is impossible to include all these within the text of each species. We have described the basic plumage sequence using the British terms:—Juvenile (J or *Juv*), first winter (*IW*), first summer (*IS*) (and for very few species second winter *2W* etc.) adult summer plumage (A or *Ad, SP*) and adult winter plumage (A or *Ad, WP*). Summer plumage is synonymous in this context with breeding or nuptial plumage and winter plumage with non-breeding plumage. These terms all refer to the plumage and hence the characters used for ageing. Various systems have been developed by ringing schemes to enable age to be coded for automatic data processing and these have complicated ageing terminology by referring to calendar years rather than age groups shown by plumage.

The codes used by the main ringing schemes are included in Table 1, together with the British and North American terminology of plumage sequence. We realise that the wording used may cause some confusion in the southern hemisphere where the southern winter occurs during the northern summer and vice versa but we hope Table 1 will clarify any difficulties.

Table 1

PLUMAGE TERMINOLOGY AND RINGING CODES USED IN EUROPE AND NORTH AMERICA

A) Terminology of plumage

J J A S O N D J F M A M J J A S O N D J F M A M J J A S O N D

European Pullus→Juv→(B)→IW→(B)→IS→(C)→Ad WP→(B)→Ad SP→(C)→Ad WP

N. America Downy→Juv→(B)→Basic 1→(B)→Alt. 1→(C)→Def. Basic→(B)→Def. Alt→(C)→Def. Basic

Notes: i) In European terminology all unaged full grown birds are FG.

ii) This is the simplest example; in several species a 2W and 2S (Basic II and Alternate II respectively) plumage is recognisable before the Ad (Definitive) plumage is attained.

iii) B = body moult, C = complete moult. The precise timing and strategy of moult varies with species.

B) Ringing codes

J J A S O N D J F M A M J J A S O N D J F M A M J J A S O N D

1) *Euring* (i) Immature

1→3J→3→
4
4(L)→2(HY)→
1(AHY)→

5→
6→
5(SY)→
6(ASY)→

7→
8
7(TY)→
8(ATY)→

(ii) Adult, age unknown

2) *N. American* (i) Immature

(ii) Adult, age unknown

after here only usable if immature with distinctive 2W plumage or soft parts.

after here only if distinctive 3W plumage or soft parts

Note: In the Euring code an unaged full-grown bird which could have been hatched in the year it was caught is coded 2, if in any unknown previous year it is 4. In North American codes they are coded 0 (U) or 1 (AHY) respectively.

16

ii) Definition of feather tracts

The standard names for feather tracts and parts of the whole bird are given in Figure 2. Parts of the wing are shown in Figure 3. In the text there are frequent references to "coverts" used without a descriptive prefix—all of these references relate to the median wing-coverts. Where reference is made to the inner median coverts (the most useful single group of feathers — outer primaries apart — for ageing waders), we refer to the innermost feathers anterior to the inner tertials. The homology of these coverts is not clear and they may represent small greater coverts — they are readily observed however. The primaries and tail feathers are numbered descendently (from inner to outer).

Figure 2 Topography of a generalised wader.

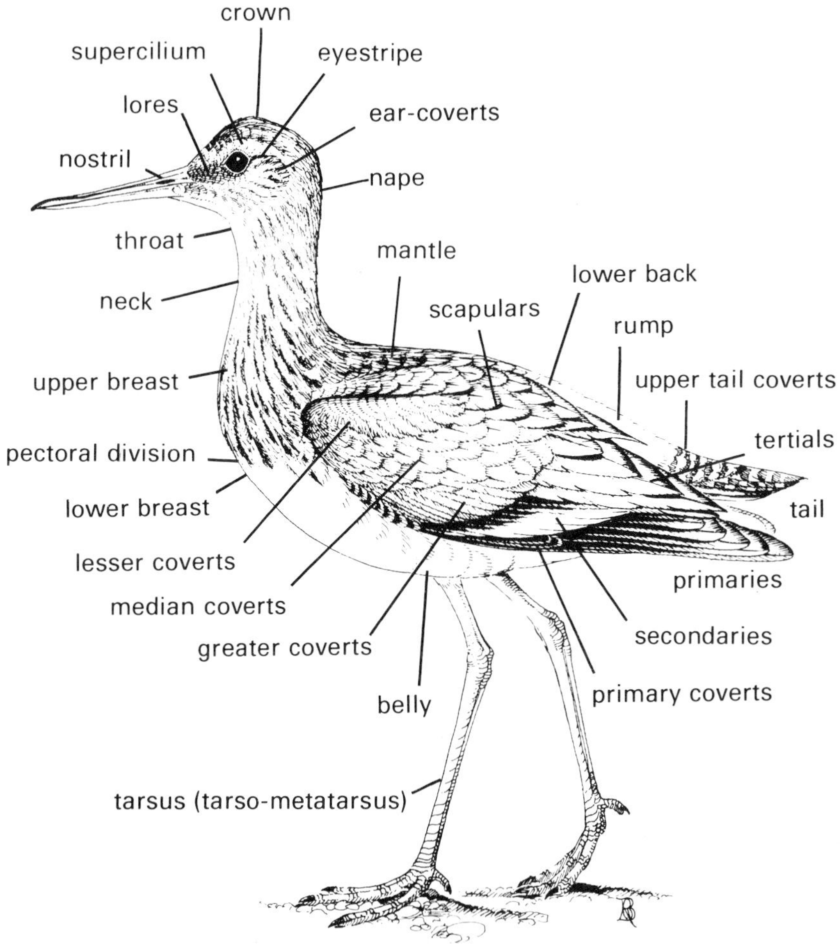

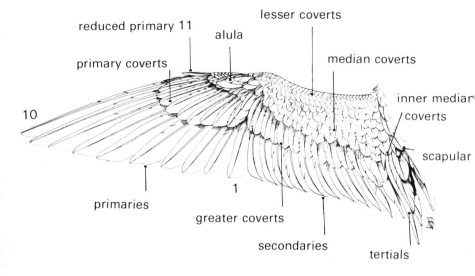

Figure 3 Nomenclature of wing feather tracts used in the text.

iii) **Terminology of the feather types**

In the description of each species standard terms are used to describe the colour patterns, and these are illustrated in Figure 4.

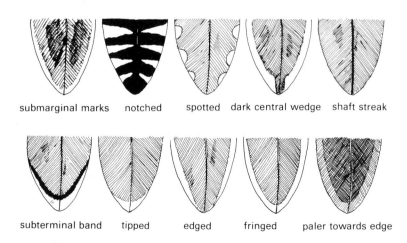

Figure 4 Nomenclature of feather patterning used in the text.

iv) Wear categories

The timing and pattern of moult is extremely important in the accurate ageing of waders. The degree of wear shown by, in particular, the outer primaries is difficult to quantify but nevertheless is extremely helpful to the observer. The four categories of wear used in the species accounts are shown in Figure 5.

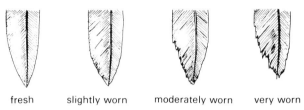

fresh   slightly worn   moderately worn   very worn

Figure 5 Categories of primary wear referred to in the text.

The pale areas on exposed feathers, such as the scapulars and tertials, wear much faster than dark areas. Even after pale spots or bars have been worn away, the original pattern of the feathers can still be seen clearly, see Figure 6. This is of particular value for *Juv/IW* birds of many species.

fresh   slightly worn   moderately worn

Figure 6 Typical pattern of wear for pale-spotted feathers.

v) Moult

Moult terminology follows Snow (1970). All references to moult, unless otherwise mentioned, refer to moult of the remiges (primaries and secondaries). All waders have 11 primaries but the outermost (11th) is almost invariably greatly reduced in size and is of little significance in the study of moult. There is variation in the numbers of secondaries (8 to 14) and tertials (5 to at least 8), according to species. In the genus *Gallinago* the number of rectrices (tail feathers) varies between 12 and 28 but most other waders have 12.

Moult usually starts with the innermost (1st) primary and progresses outwards. When primary moult is about half completed the outermost (1st) secondary is dropped and moult progresses towards the body. The tertials are replaced soon after and in most waders the innermost secondaries are then renewed and moult proceeds in two directions towards the centre of the secondaries. The rectrices are replaced during the secondary moult, usually by progression from the middle (1st) feathers towards the edge of the tail.

after normal moult (with moderately worn primaries)

suspended moult

arrested moult

moult completed after suspension

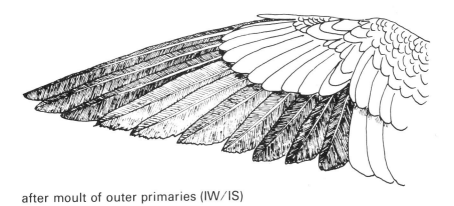

after moult of outer primaries (IW/IS)

Figure 7 Some primary moult patterns shown by waders.

Typically primary moult spans the entire period of the replacement of remiges and rectrices. Tertials are also frequently replaced during the partial body moult.

In waders there are three basic patterns of remex moult. Firstly, most adults have a complete, uninterrupted moult during the autumn or winter, related to date, period and distance of migration. Secondly, in many species adult birds start to moult in northern areas, suspend and then complete it in the wintering grounds. The term *suspend* has been used in preference to *arrest* in this guide as virtually all species that interrupt moult in this way, do complete it during the following few months. Only the largest species, especially *Haematopus ostralegus*, show on occasions unmoulted outer primaries which may be retained for up to two years (*arrested* moult). The third moult pattern occurs

21

fairly widely among first winter birds which migrate to the southern hemisphere, and involves the replacement of outer primaries and inner secondaries only. Some first winter birds undertake a complete normal descendent primary moult.

Moult in progress is itself a very valuable key to age in all species where the patterns of moult differ between ages. For species such as Common Sandpiper *Actitis hypoleucos* and Little Stint *Calidris minuta*, where juveniles often undertake a full primary moult in the first winter, other clues such as retained coverts, shape and extent of wear of unmoulted primaries and moult season must be used.

The pattern of wear along a completely full-grown set of primaries can be very illuminating (see Figure 7). In a juvenile wing, where all the primaries are grown at the same time, wear tends to increase from the protected inner primaries towards the outers. There may be a sudden increase in wear on those feathers extending beyond the tertials on the folded wing, and in species with rounded wings the outermost primaries may be protected from wear. In many species some primaries (usually inners) are tipped pale, and these wear faster than corresponding wholly dark feathers, thus tending to blur the wear pattern slightly.

The same features may be seen in the wing of an adult bird which has completed a full primary moult, but with them the wear is initially more uniform, as the inner primaries are of course several weeks older than the newer outer ones. This may be particularly noticeable in birds which have moulted very slowly, where there may be the unique appearance of decreasing wear from inners to outers. In birds having completed moult after a suspension, there are two gradients of wear and often a clear division at the point where the moult was suspended.

When an adult bird has completed moult in spring following a suspension over the winter, and shows a group of outer primaries clearly newer than the inner feathers, there may be the possibility of confusion with a first year bird in those species where outer primaries only are renewed towards the end of the first winter. However, in such first winter birds the unmoulted inner primaries are much more worn than the corresponding feathers of the adult, and the young bird can be told by the much greater contrast between the old and new feathers. Further, the unmoulted feathers often show a gradient of wear in the young bird, increasing towards the outermost old primary, whereas these feathers of the adult will in general be evenly worn.

It is almost always easy to distinguish adults from young birds with this pattern of wear, but it may be more difficult to decide whether an adult showing outer primaries newer than the inners suspended during the winter or had a protracted active moult instead.

In actively moulting birds, first summer (second autumn) individuals can usually be distinguished by considerably greater wear on the unmoulted outer feathers compared with the younger and more wear-resistant unmoulted feathers of the adult. However the situation is complicated by those birds which replaced their outer primaries (only) during the first winter, so that some or all of the remaining unmoulted feathers may be quite fresh, and by those rare adults which arrested the full moult in the previous season and retained some very worn outers from the previous generation of feathers.

In this guide we have attempted to describe the main moult periods and to indicate where variability occurs. In the space available it is not possible to expand the accounts to cover every eventuality. Species which have a large latitudinal wintering range are subjected to wide contrasts in climatic conditions, combined with extended migration periods, and exhibit considerable variation in their moult patterns. Work on this subject is still in its infancy and knowledge incomplete, so therefore extra care should be exercised when ageing waders wintering in the tropics or the southern hemisphere.

d) **Sexing**

Where possible the larger sex is indicated. It is rare to be able to sex every bird from measurements and this is particularly true of juveniles and immatures. There is a general tendency for females ($\female$) to be larger than males ($\male$), but there are many species where this is reversed. Few plumage criteria separate the sexes and these apply almost exclusively to summer plumage. With few exceptions the $\male$ is generally brighter and the $\female$ duller with less well-defined areas of colour. In most species birds can only be safely sexed on plumage characters when a breeding pair is examined together. No mention has been made of brood patches (bare vascularised abdominal areas developed for incubation) as few data are available. More information is needed on this topic.

e) **Geographical variation**

Most species with a large or discontinuous range show some degree of variation in size and plumage which can be related to specific breeding areas. These differences, if relatively constant, enable the species to be divided into subspecies or races. Among waders, races usually differ only slightly in their average sizes, while summer plumage colour variations can often only be determined by comparison with an extensive collection of specimens. When the breeding range is continuous there are clines in the continuously variable characters of differentiation, such as summer plumage colouration or measurements, and therefore many, probably most, individuals cannot (and should not) be definitely ascribed to a particular race, especially with sexual differences as a further complication. The opposite ends of clinal variations are, however, often readily determinable, and where the breeding range is discontinuous races may be relatively easy to separate.

In this guide we have included those races accepted by Vaurie (1965) for the Palaearctic and Godfrey (1966) for the Nearctic plus additional more recent work. Thus only the more marked elements of geographical variation are included here.

f) **Biometrics**

All measurements are given in millimetres, and weights (where included) are in grams.

The methods used to measure specimens are shown in Figure 8 and follow the techniques used in the field in most countries (e.g. Spencer 1976). In addition to the standard technique of bill measurement, a variant now coming into use is the nalospi which is the distance from the anterior edge of the nostril opening to bill tip. This measurement has a very close relationship to bill length and can be useful when feather wear makes the bill/feather margin difficult to determine. Details of other special measurements used on individual species are described in the text of that species. The measurements are set out in a standard form, i.e.

sample size, age, sex, range, average

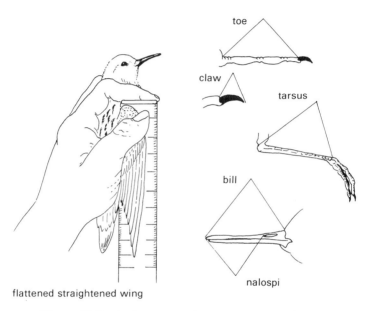

flattened straightened wing

Figure 8 Techniques used to measure waders.

Where sample sizes are small or where few birds in the collection had been sexed, ages or sexes have been combined. This is noted at the top of the section. We have not divided biometrics by time of year, and seasonal variations in bill and wing lengths such as those demonstrated by Pienkowski (1976) and Pienkowski and Minton (1973) should be borne in mind. Weight is much more variable, and has not been included except in special cases.

The measurements are all obtained from museum specimens and certain of these differ materially from those of live birds; however, because many species have not been caught and measured alive it was considered best to make all of the sections comparable. Where data from other sources have been included they have been obtained by a similar technique to those used by us and the source has been stated. Of the principal measurements given, bill and tarsus length do not differ significantly from fresh measurements and can therefore be readily used by field workers. However winglength is significantly shorter in dried museum specimens than in fresh birds. Figure 9 shows the difference between the two sets of measurements, based on our sample and live birds measured by members (with known standardised measuring ability) of the Wash Wader Ringing Group. There is a fairly close relationship between the measurements, and they differed by between 1.0% and 3.0%. The live measurements of all species can be estimated by comparison of the winglengths with Figure 9.

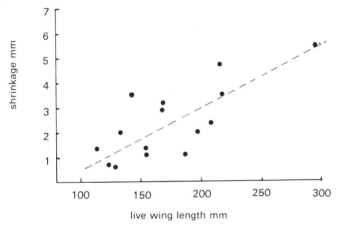

Figure 9 Relationship between winglength of live birds measured by the Wash Wader Ringing Group (horizontal axis) and the shortening indicated by museum samples (vertical axis). The line is fitted by eye.

Museum collections contain many birds which have been sexed and these have formed the basis for the biometric section. However it is well known that some, and it can be over 25% in immatures, are incorrectly sexed. We have not arbitrarily discounted the 'obviously' wrongly sexed birds, and their inclusion has the effect of increasing the range and variability of the measurements of each sex and of making the averages closer to each other than the putative true values.

The main use of this section is to indicate where there are separations in size, as an aid for the analysis of field collected data. Because of the inherent variability introduced by incorrect sexing, standard deviations of the measurements are not given. It is hoped that in future editions of the guide, when much larger samples will have been measured, the SD will be included. Unless specifically mentioned, the measurements presented refer to the species or race as a whole; in many cases geographical variation exists but the measurements do not refer to any single part of the birds' range.

g) References

These are given at the end of each species account, by numbers. The number refers to Section B of the references listed at the end of the guide. We have not included titles of papers but have indicated which aspects of relevance are detailed in them. The following subject headings are used—identification, ageing, moult, sexing, measurements, weight and geographical variation. References to weights have been included separately because they are excluded from the biometric sections. General reference works which have been consulted frequently are given in Section A of the references and not included after each species.

GENERAL WAYS OF AGEING WADERS

The general principles for ageing waders are few and relatively simple. Those most useful for each species are described in their accounts; there are, no doubt, many other additional features which may help in difficult cases. The main ways of identifying juvenile and immature waders are summarised below:

a) Primaries

Juveniles have rather paler brown primaries when compared with the dark blackish-brown of adults. The primaries also tend to be pointed and relatively narrow in contrast to the broader, more rounded adult types. Tail feathers and secondaries also follow these trends. Because of their weaker structure the feathers wear much faster than those of adults, so once the fledging and adult moult periods are known, the relative state of wear of primaries (Figure 5) enables almost every bird to be aged.

The use of patterns of wear along the primaries for ageing has been described in the section on moult.

b) General plumage

Juveniles tend to have a soft plumage which may be readily appreciated in the hand, and often pale buff spots or fringes to feathers of the upperparts. The retention of the buff on the inner median coverts (where they are protected from sunlight and excessive wear by the scapulars), provides another basic method of identifying immature birds. Regular fault bars (see Svensson 1975 for details), especially on the tail, and tail down (or its breakage zone) are also indicative of juveniles.

c) Structural

Young birds usually have shorter wings and bills than adults but measurements are rarely diagnostic.

There are three anatomical techniques which are of general use for ageing birds and which are of some help in ageing waders. They are not applicable to live birds, but are mentioned here as accurately sexed and aged material, with standardised measurements, is so scarce that anyone able to obtain these data is strongly urged to do so. The methods are:

(i) **Bursa Fabricius:** this small sac, present only in immatures, leads off the dorsal side of the cloaca and protrudes into the peritoneal cavity. In waders, unlike some other species groups, it has no external opening. In juveniles it may be over 1 cm long but during the late autumn it rapidly regresses and by winter is absent on some first winter birds; it has usually completely disappeared by the next summer (see McNeil and Burton 1972).

(ii) **Cranial pneumatisation:** a technique of use for passerines but of very limited value for waders. Juveniles have a smaller area of pneumatised bone but by winter they may have almost any degree of pneumatisation. Adults retain some cartilage, particularly on the fronto-parietal bones. As patterns are variable and overlapping in winter they are of little help. (See Harrison 1957, McNeil and Burton 1972).

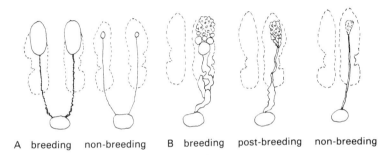

A   breeding   non-breeding   B   breeding   post-breeding   non-breeding

Figure 10 Reproductive tracts of waders: A male, B female. Note that they are viewed here from the ventral surface, as would be seen on dissection. The area of the kidneys is the dashed line.

(iii) **Gonadal development:** in and just prior to the breeding season mature birds have greatly enlarged gonads, and this includes breeding first summer birds. It is usually possible to recognise regressed glands during the autumn migration by their larger size and in females by the wide convoluted oviduct and decidedly granular ovaries. In winter the regression continues so that in females the oviduct is relatively thin and straight. In immature birds the oviduct is also thin and straight (see Figure 10, which also shows how to sex birds). In view of the similarity in structure during winter, when plumage characters are sometimes less easy, this technique too is of very limited use.

ACKNOWLEDGEMENTS

We are greatly indebted to all those who, over many years, have gathered much of the information that is presented in this guide. They are much too numerous to name but their efforts were invaluable. We would, however, like to specifically thank all of those who have aided the production, in particular Dr D. W. Snow and his staff of the British Museum of Natural History, Tring, for help and permission to work on their collection of waders. Professor F. A. Pitelka provided similar facilities at Berkeley, University of California. Dr W. G. Hale at Liverpool Polytechnic and his research students J. Greenwood, P. Rose, Mrs. S. Rynn and R. Taylor provided extensive and as yet unpublished material on biometrics and geographical variation.

Extensive comments on the text and other help were also given by F. B. Argyle, Dr J. S. Ash, I. P. Bainbridge, Drs G. C. Boere, M. Bradstreet, Dr P. J. Dare, M. Fletcher, A. O. Folkestad, G. H. Green, Dr O. Hilden, Prof T. R. Howell, R. Hudson, A. R. Johnson, R. H. Loyn, Dr C. D. T. Minton, Dr R. I. G. Morrison, P. Morgan, P. Myers, D. Nethersole-Thompson, G. Page, Dr D. J. Pearson, M. W. Pienkowski, Dr C. S. Robbins, J. M. Rochford, A. Spaans, B. Stronach, Dr R. W. Summers, A. J. Tree, K. Williamson, J. G. Walmsley, M. Waltner, Dr D. Wells and J. Wilson.

The superb text photographs were taken by J. B. and S. Bottomley. We would like to thank them for providing material which greatly aids the understanding of the species accounts. Dr V. Flint provided the frontispiece photographs, and the drawings are by K. Baker, R. Bishop and the authors. N. Arlott kindly provided the two vignettes.

The text was typed by Mrs C. Adlem, Mrs G. Bonham, Mrs E. Murray, Mrs H. Pearson, Mrs D. Rushton and Miss S. Woodman and our thanks go to them also.

PAINTED SNIPE   *Rostratula benghalensis*

SC, SE and ME P. Resident or short-distance migrant (E, A, O).

IDENTIFICATION   Strikingly-patterned snipe-like bird, mainly greenish above and white below with greyish or chestnut neck and breast. Bill brown, greenish at base, shortish with decurved tip. Legs dull yellow to greyish-green. Slightly rounded wings with large golden-buff spots across primaries. Clear sexual dimorphism in post-juvenile plumages.

AGEING   Because of striking patterns ♂ can be confused with juvenile. Only character found was covert pattern (illustrated below).

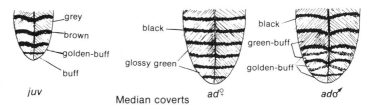

Median coverts

Juv   Coverts relatively small. They replace most coverts within a few months of fledging but some, usually inner medians, are retained.

IW   ♀ easier as retained coverts contrast in pattern to new *Ad* types. *IW*♂ needs care.

Presence of tail down and absence of blackish breastband also indicates *Juv* but not *IW*.

SEXING   Clearly dimorphic, see table below.

	wing (African)	neck/mantle	breast	coverts	scapulars
♂	133	brownish-grey	grey-brown/ white	spotted golden-buff	no white
♀	135	reddish-brown	reddish-brown	barred green/black	much white

GEOGRAPHICAL VARIATION   Two races recognised: *R.b. australis* (Australia) and *R.b. benghalensis* (rest). In nominate race Chinese birds have wings c3mm shorter, bills similar and tarsi slightly shorter than African ones. *R.b. australis* has larger wing (5A♂ x̄ 146.2; 5A♀ x̄ 155.6) and shorter bill and tarsus.

BIOMETRICS   N & E African birds only.

Wing	16 A♂	125-133	(130.7)	:	7 J♂	130-133	(131.9)
	18 A♀	134-146	(140.0)	:	5 J♀	137-146	(140.6)
Bill	16 A♂	43-51	(47.6)	:	6 J♂	43-45	(43.8)
	17 A♀	46-54	(50.2)	:	5 J♀	47-52	(49.4)
Tarsus	16 A♂	40-47	(44.0)	:	7 J♂	40-46	(42.7)
	18 A♀	44-50	(46.9)	:	5 J♀	46-48	(46.6)

OYSTERCATCHER *Haematopus ostralegus*

W, MC and ME P. Resident or short- to medium-distance migrant.

IDENTIFICATION Large pied wader with, in adult, orange-red bill, pink legs, red iris and orange-red eyering. Upperparts and head black, with broad white wingbar and white lower back, rump and upper tail coverts. Black terminal band to tail. Breast black, sometimes with whitish band (collar) across throat, rest of underparts white. *See Plate 1.*

AGEING (based on Dare *in litt*).

Ad SP Upperparts, including all of neck, glossy black. Coverts black. Iris deep red; bill and eyering bright orange-red, although bill paler and yellower at tip; legs pink.

WP Upperparts and coverts duller black. Neck with irregular white collar. Eyering duller; iris red; bill duller orange but often slightly dusky towards tip. Legs pale pink, often with dusky suffusion. Moult August-December. Primaries fresh midwinter, slightly worn spring.

Juv Upperparts, especially coverts, brownish-black with brownish-buff fringes. Upper tail coverts barred brown and tipped buff. Neck collar absent or very indistinct. Iris brown; no clear eyering; bill dull orange-yellow at base becoming dark horn/slate distally. Legs pale grey.

IW Upperparts brownish-black with buff fringes wearing; some left on inner median and upper tail coverts through winter. Broad white neck collar. Iris brown, becoming yellowish. Bill orange with dusky brown distal half. Legs grey becoming darkish slate. Primaries fairly worn in winter, very worn and faded by spring.

IS White collar; dull iris, bill and legs.

2W/3W The soft parts become steadily brighter with age; sometimes it is possible to age accurately *2W* and *3W* birds; often, however, they should be classed as immatures. Upperparts black but with large white neck collar all year round. Iris pale reddish with brownish wash on upper half at first, becoming dull red. Eyering yellowish with orange suffusion developing. Bill with orange-red basal half, distal half becoming medium horn and later with reddish wash. Legs darkish grey, later with pink suffusion.

SEXING Bill length and shape appear to be the only characters. ♂ has shorter but deeper bill than ♀ (depth at deepest part). In breeding pairs studied in Britain there was 5-10mm difference in bill length with ♂ smaller than ♀. The difference occurs in *IW* and *2W/3W* birds as well, as shown below for samples from N.W. England.

	IW	2W/3W	Ad
♂	13 : 62-72 (67.5) :	31 : 64-74 (70.9) :	84 : 64-81 (71.4)
♀	15 : 70-82 (78.0) :	31 : 73-86 (79.1) :	82 : 65-87 (79.8)

31

As there is geographical variation in bill length, the above figures do not represent all populations.

GEOGRAPHICAL VARIATION   The systematic relations within the genus *Haematopus* are unclear. Here the Nearctic birds are considered separately and three Palaearctic races are recognised: *H.o. ostralegus* (Europe and W. USSR), *H.o. longipes* (west central USSR), and *H.o. osculans* (E. USSR). Bill length and to some extent wing and tarsus length increase from west to east. *Osculans* has black shafts to outer 3 primaries (others have white). *Longipes* differs from *ostralegus* in that the groove in the upper mandible is more than half the bill length, and in the generally paler and browner mantle.

BIOMETRICS   *H.o. ostralegus* (for bill length see Sexing).

Wing	34 A♂	245-272	(259.0)	:	13 J♂	235-263	(249.9)
	30 A♀	249-277	(259.8)	:	17 J♀	235-266	(248.9)
Tarsus	34 A♂	47-56	(50.6)	:	13 J♂	47-54	(49.1)
	33 A♀	46-54	(49.7)	:	16 J♀	45-55	(49.5)

Insufficient sample of *H.o. longipes* examined but bill 69-101 and tarsus 51-60 reported. Winglength apparently as *H.o. ostralegus*.

H.o. osculans

Wing	11 A	260-284	(270.9)	:	15 J	244-275	(260.7)
Bill	12 A	79-99	(90.0)	:	15 J	71-102	(86.1)
Tarsus	12 A	49-60	(53.9)	:	15 J	51-57	(53.7)

REFERENCES   Age 3, 19, Moult 20, 119, Sex 3, 56, 166, Biometrics 49, 97, Weight 49, 90, 92, 97.

AMERICAN OYSTERCATCHER
Haematopus palliatus

Coastal M and S N. Resident or short-distance migrant (N).

IDENTIFICATION   Always from *H. ostralegus* by dark back, leaving only a narrow white rump-band, and by brown tone to upperparts contrasting with black head, neck and breastband. Never has white throat band. Adults have lemon-yellow iris with orange-red eyering.

AGEING

Ad   Coverts uniform brown although some feathers tipped whitish when fresh. Bill clear bright red with yellowish tip, iris lemon-yellow and eyering orange-red (soft parts probably less bright in winter). Legs pink. Moult in autumn, so primaries are fresh in winter and slightly worn in spring.

Juv Upperparts, including black head, extensively spotted pale buff; the spots are bordered by dark brown. Bill orange at base but otherwise dark horn. (Probably iris dull brown and legs greyish).

IW Spots abrade rapidly and in winter are only present on inner medians, some of which are retained to spring. Bill orange at base with dull outer half. Primaries fairly worn in midwinter, moderately worn in spring. Primary moult often starts April/May.

IS Active wing moult, with retained primaries very worn. It is possible, but could not be checked, that colour of bill follows pattern in *H. ostralegus* and that iris becomes steadily brighter yellow with age. If so *2W* birds should be distinguishable.

SEXING ♀ averages slightly larger than ♂.

BIOMETRICS

Wing	9 A♂	243-267	(256.1)	: 8 J	252-275	(261.2)
	7 A♀	249-269	(261.1)	:		
Bill	11 A♂	69-85	(79.7)	: 8 J	69-93	(80.7)
	7 A♀	74-95	(88.0)	:		
Tarsus	12 A♂	52-63	(55.7)	: 9 J	54-66	(59.4)
	7 A♀	55-68	(58.6)	:		

AMERICAN BLACK OYSTERCATCHER
Haematopus bachmani

Coastal W N. Resident or short-distance migrant (N).

IDENTIFICATON Plumage all blackish-brown. From *H. moquini* by lemon-yellow iris with orange eyering, and browner mantle.

AGEING

Ad SP Head and neck black. Mantle and coverts mid-brown, underparts uniform brownish. Bill bright scarlet with yellowish tip, iris clear lemon-yellow and legs pinkish-white at all seasons.

WP Mantle and coverts dark brown; underparts blackish-brown with extensive whitish tips. Moult July-October; primaries fresh in winter, slightly worn in spring.

Juv Mantle and coverts blackish-brown with dull buff tips. Bill with orange-brown base grading to blackish distal half; iris yellowish-brown; eyering orange. Legs brownish.

IW Only inner medians retain buff tips to mid-winter. Bill and iris become progressively brighter. Primaries fairly worn in winter, moderately worn in spring.

IS Moderately worn primaries, but moult is May-August. Iris and bill reported to reach adult brightness with this moult.

SEXING ♀ reported to average larger than ♂ at all ages.

BIOMETRICS Only 7 birds examined — all measurements combined.

Wing 254-266 (259.8) : Bill 71-81 (74.4) : Tarsus 52-56 (53.7)

REFERENCES Age, Moult, Sex, Biometrics 165.

AFRICAN BLACK OYSTERCATCHER
Haematopus moquini

SW P (Canaries) now probably extinct there (E).

IDENTIFICATION Typical oystercatcher but plumage all black or blackish-brown, sometimes with a small white flash on inner primaries. From *H. bachmani* by red (not yellow) iris, and less brown on mantle. Also slightly larger, with wing usually 270+.

AGEING Plumage sequence similar to other *Haematopus*, with distinct *Juv* fringes. In *Ad* bill is red with orange tip, iris red, eyering broad and orange, and legs pink; *Juv* has bill with base orange-red below and orange-brown above and dark brown distal half, iris brown, eyering narrow and dark orange, and legs grey. The *Juv* colours probably become steadily brighter with age as in other *Haematopus*.

SEXING No data available.

BIOMETRICS and **GEOGRAPHICAL VARIATION** Very few examined. The ranges of 7 from S. Africa and 2 (*Ad*) from the Canaries are presented below.

	Wing		Bill		Tarsus
S. Africa	269-301	:	58-89	:	53-56
Canaries	260-264	:	72-81	:	53-54

REFERENCES Ageing, Weight, Moult 143B.

IBISBILL
Ibidorhyncha struthersii

SE P. Resident or short-distance migrant.

IDENTIFICATION Shape and size recalling *Numenius phaeopus* but has contrasting plumage with mainly grey upperparts and white underparts. Black crown, face and throat, outlined in white. Narrow black breastband bordered above by white line. Conspicuous white band across primaries; rump and tail with blackish bands. Decurved scarlet-red bill, legs pinkish-grey or red.

AGEING

Ad SP Face black. Upperparts and coverts uniform brownish-grey. Upper breast grey with white upper and black lower breastbands. Legs blood-red.

34

WP Similar but face pattern less distinct due to whitish-tipped feathers. Legs pinkish-grey. Apparently long moulting period (autumn to early spring) would make primary wear difficult to use.

Juv Face brownish. Upperparts and coverts brownish-grey with extensive pale buff/orange-buff tips. Breastband brownish, lacking white upper line.

IW As *Ad WP* but some buff-tipped coverts, especially inner medians, are retained to spring. Throat whiter than *Ad*. Primaries fairly worn midwinter, moderately worn spring.

IS Only the most worn birds can be told on the primaries, but a few may retain buff-tipped inner medians. Face as *Ad*.

SEXING ♀ reported larger than ♂ (bills of ⩾ 75 being ♀).

BIOMETRICS All birds combined (few sexed specimens examined).

Wing	14 A	232-247	(240.4)	:	9 J	230-240	(236.2)
Bill	15 A	68-83	(74.9)	:	9 J	60-79	(70.1)
Tarsus	15 A	44-51	(47.3)	:	9 J	46-49	(47.2)

BLACK-WINGED STILT   *Himantopus himantopus*

SW and SC P. Resident or short-distance migrant. (E, O, A).

IDENTIFICATION White plumage except for brownish or black back, black wings above and below, and also sometimes blackish or dusky on crown and nape. Axillaries white. Tail pale grey-brown. Slender black bill and immensely long pinkish-red legs. Juveniles much browner with pinkish-grey legs. See *H. mexicanus*.

AGEING

Ad SP Mantle and coverts uniformly black, or mantle brown and coverts black. Secondaries evenly blackish. Tip of web of inner primary with small pale grey edge. Crown and nape white or with variable amount of blackish.

WP Primary moult July/August to November/December. Plumage as *SP* but crown and nape grey-brown. Primaries always appear relatively fresh.

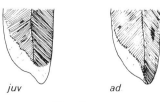

juv   ad

7th primary

Juv All of upperparts and underwing coverts extensively tipped and notched pale reddish-buff. Inner primaries tipped white and secondaries with broad white tips.

IW As *WP Ad♀* in having brown mantle. Coverts, especially inner medians, retain buff fringes to spring. White tips to secondaries and inner primaries. Primaries moderately worn by winter.

IS Only worn primaries and white-tipped remiges distinguish from *Ad♀*. Primary moult can start in May, but some do not complete until early winter so retaining some white-tipped secondaries throughout the second autumn.

SEXING

Ad *plumage* ♂. Back black. Colour of crown and nape a guide — usually black or white.

♀ Back brown, contrasting with black coverts. Crown and nape usually with dusky tips to white feathers. (NB: all colour patterns of crown and nape occur in both sexes).

Size ♂ usually larger with wing ⩾ 240, tarsus ⩾ 125.
♀ usually with wing ⩽ 235, tarsus ⩽ 115.

Juv/IW *plumage* ♂ coverts with dull metallic green gloss.
♀ coverts largely without metallic green gloss, although a few outermost may have some gloss on outer webs.

Size Much more overlap than in adults but tarsus a good guide. Usually ⩾ 120 are ♂, ⩽ 115 ♀.

IS Size distinction as above. ♂ gains some black mantle feathers by early summer.

GEOGRAPHICAL VARIATION Apparently little in Palaearctic although extra-limital races have some plumage and biometric variations.

BIOMETRICS

Wing	42 A♂	230-255	(243.0)	:	9 J♂	207-226	(218.6)
	34 A♀	220-242	(230.6)	:	11 J♀	206-224	(215.4)
Bill	63 A	56-69	(63.6)	:	18 J	57-69	(62.6)
Tarsus	43 A♂	107-137	(124.7)	:	9 J♂	115-134	(124.8)
	32 A♀	100-124	(111.8)	:	12 J♀	100-119	(111.7)

BLACK-NECKED STILT   *Himantopus mexicanus*

s N. Resident or short-distance migrant. (N).

IDENTIFICATION Post-juveniles from *H. himantopus* (of which it may only be a race) by extensive black or nearly black crown, mark around eye, and back of neck. ♂ in *SP* has pink-tinged underparts.

AGEING

Ad   Mantle and coverts uniformly black, or mantle dark brown and coverts black. Primaries and secondaries uniformly blackish. Moult in autumn; primaries are fresh in winter and only slightly worn in spring.

8th primary

juv

Juv   Upperparts, including coverts, brown with extensive pale reddish-buff fringes. Secondaries and inner primaries with whitish tips.

IW   Upperparts brown; buff-fringed inner medians retained to spring. Secondaries and inner primaries with whitish tips. Primaries slightly worn in winter, moderately worn in spring.

IS   As *IW* but retained coverts less easy to see. Primaries very worn.

SEXING

Ad   ♂ has black back, continuous with black neck; underparts tinged rosy-pink in *SP*. ♀ has back brown, contrasting with black neck and coverts; underparts always white.

IS   Only possible to sex some IS ♂ which have started body moult and gained some black feathers on mantle.

All ages   ♂ larger than ♀ but some overlap in all measurements. Best characters for separation of *Ad* are wing division at 220 and tarsus division 107. ♂ is also heavier.

BIOMETRICS from Hamilton (1975): all adult, ranges not given.

Wing	18♂	(225.1)	Tarsus	18♂	(113.0)
	21♀	(214.7)		21♀	(103.2)
Bill	17♂	(65.3)	Weight	6♂	(177.0)
	19♀	(63.5)		12♀	(160.3)

REFERENCES Biometrics 48, Weight 48, 87.

AVOCET   *Recurvirostra avosetta*

SW and SC P. Resident or short-, medium- or long-distance migrant. (E, O).

IDENTIFICATION Strikingly-patterned mainly white wader with black or brownish cap, back of neck, band along scapulars, band across coverts, and outer primaries. Greater coverts, secondaries, alula and inner primaries white. White of mantle sometimes suffused pale grey. Bill black, slender, strongly upcurved. Longish blue-grey legs.

AGEING

Ad   Cap and nape black or blackish-brown. Generally all other dark areas blackish. Primaries 4-10 (outer seven) blackish, and 3 with large whitish patch on inner web. Moult July-January, (most August to November), so primaries fresh in winter, slightly worn in spring. In winter some-times cap of ♀ with some whitish feathers.

5th primary

juv   *ad*

Juv   Cap pale sepia. Extensive brownish-buff edges to both white and darkish feathers of upperparts. Pattern of white on primaries distinctive:- 7-10 (outer four) all dark brown (paler than *Ad*), 6 sometimes all dark but often with palish edge on tip of inner web, 5 always with whitish edge, 4 has large white area.

IW   Cap may be dark brown but always paler than *Ad*. Most buff-tipped inner medians moulted during late autumn but usually some are retained to spring. Pattern of white in primaries as *Juv*. Primaries wear rapidly so are moderately worn by spring.

IS   Some have retained inner medians, but best told by very worn primaries with characteristic pattern of white.

SEXING   No characters found but iris colour (Witherby *et al*) reported to help— ♂ red-brown; ♀ brown.

GEOGRAPHICAL VARIATION   No races recognised, (but indications from a very small sample that birds in SE Europe and SW Asia are slightly larger than W European birds).

BIOMETRICS

Wing	28 A	218-238	(226.6)	:	21 J	211-232	(221.7)
Bill	17 A	75-89	(83.2)	:	13 J	73-88	(80.6)
Tarsus	27 A	75-96	(86.1)	:	22 J	65-95	(83.2)

AMERICAN AVOCET   *Recurvirostra americana*

MW and MC N. Short-distance migrant.

IDENTIFICATION   Always from *R. avosetta* by black or blackish outer half of wing, with extensive black on inner primaries and outer secondaries, and by lack of dark cap and nape. Greater coverts blackish, tipped white. Head and neck mainly orange-brown in summer, grey in winter.

AGEING

Ad SP Head and neck orange-brown. Primaries 3-10 (outer eight) all black, 2 usually dark but may have a pale edge to tip of inner web.

WP Head and neck grey. Coverts uniform. Primary pattern as above. Moult August-November; primaries fresh in winter, slightly worn in spring.

Juv Head and neck suffused pale pinkish-chestnut. Mantle and coverts with brownish-buff tips. Primaries brown, always appearing moderately worn. Pattern of white on primaries characteristic: 6-10 (outer five) brown, 5 and 4 sometimes dark but 4 always has pale tip to inner web, 3 and 2 with increasing area of white.

IW Head and neck colour moulted out starting from forehead to become as *Ad WP*. Some buff-tipped inner medians retained to spring. Primary pattern as *Juv*, and primaries moderately worn.

IS Only by very worn brown primaries, the pattern of white only sometimes still clear. Most attain *SP*.

ad♂

ad♀

SEXING *SP* Some ♀ paler than ♂

size ♂ generally larger.

bill shape Complete sexual dimorphism: ♂ is longer, but less curved, while ♀ is shorter and strongly curved. The measurement of chord gives almost complete separation, with most ♂ > 90.5 and most ♀ < 90.5, but if bill is traced on paper and radius of distal arc calculated, then plotting radius against chord gives complete separation.

BIOMETRICS from Hamilton (1975) — $\bar{x}$ of adults.

Wing	42♂	(224.6)	:	Tarsus	42♂	(98.0)
	36♀	(224.6)	:		37♀	(92.2)
Bill	36♂	(95.3)	:	Weight	16♂	(323.4)
	35♀	(86.3)	:		17♀	(309.8)

REFERENCES Sex 40, Biometrics, Weight 48.

CRAB PLOVER

Dromas ardeola

SC P. Resident or short- to medium-distance migrant (E, O).

IDENTIFICATION Adult plumage recalls *Recurvirostra* but more massively built with shorter blue-grey or grey legs and diagnostic huge black bill with deep gonys. Mainly white with black back, primaries, secondaries, primary and greater coverts. Back grey in juveniles. Crown and nape streaked grey-brown in juvenile and winter plumage and white of upperparts suffused pale grey-brown. Tail grey-brown.

AGEING

Ad SP Black back, white crown.

WP Black back, crown pale grey with indistinct darker grey-brown smudges. Moult is apparently very slow, mostly late May to late January; primaries fresh in winter, slightly worn in spring.

Juv Back and coverts pale grey, crown grey with grey-black shaft streaks.

IW Back becomes darker grey-black towards spring. Crown as *Juv*. Primaries moderately worn by mid-winter.

IS Only by very worn primaries.

SEXING No characters found.

BIOMETRICS Sexes combined.

Wing	44 A	203-226	(213.6)	: 17 J	191-219	(210.9)
Bill	50 A	51-64	(58.9)	: 19 J	41-61	(55.8)
Tarsus	51 A	87-102	(93.5)	: 22 J	84-99	(93.8)

STONE CURLEW

Burhinus oedicnemus

SW and SC P. Resident or short- to medium-distance migrant (O).

IDENTIFICATION Large sandy and brown streaked wader with large yellow eye. Usually terrestrial. Two fairly distinct white bars across coverts, each bordered black. Some black and white at sides of wedge-shaped tail. Primaries and secondaries blackish with white band across outer primaries. Outer half of bill black, base yellow. Legs yellow, with prominent joints. Longest undertail coverts tinged cinnamon.

AGEING Difficult to age, especially in south of range, as adults show much individual and geographical variation. Characters of help are:

Median coverts and tertials.

Juv Most are washed sepia with darkish subterminal bars; inner medians buffish with distinct bright buff fringe. Sometimes inners are retained to winter. *Ad* more uniform, grey-brown, more rounded. This often works in Europe, but in the south with several colour morphs it can be very difficult.

juv   ad

greater coverts   tail down

Greater coverts

Juv Tend to have broad white tips. *Ad* narrow white band wearing to black tip. Difficult after midwinter.

Tail Down

Juv May be present to September; later, tail distinctly notched at tip, where down has broken off (useful to midwinter). *Ad* smooth new tail feathers.

Moult and primary wear

Ad Moult August-November so are fresh in winter, moderately worn by late winter/spring. *Juv/IW* Primaries moderately worn in winter.

SEXING No characters found.

GEOGRAPHICAL VARIATION Five races in region: *B.o. oedicnemus* (Europe), *B.o. harterti* (S. Russia to Afghanistan), *B.o. saharae* (N. Africa, E. Mediterranean), *B.o. insularum* (E. Canaries), and *B.o. distinctus* (W. Canaries). The last two are sedentary and very local, and both are small with wing 210-236mm. The first three are distinguished by *oedicnemus* being streaked dark brown, *harterti* paler and greyer, and *saharae* more sandy. All are of similar size. *B.o. indicus*, extralimital, is small (wing 200-230) and dark.

BIOMETRICS *B.o. oedicnemus*

Wing	22 A	229-255	(239.7)	: 17 J	224-255	(240.3)
Bill	23 A	33-41	(38.4)	: 17 J	35-41	(37.6)
Tarsus	23 A	68-83	(75.7)	: 17 J	67-83	(73.9)

REFERENCES Variation 157.

SENEGAL THICK-KNEE   *Burhinus senegalensis*

SC P. Mainly resident (E).

IDENTIFICATION Similar to *B. oedicnemus*, but smaller than all races occurring in region, and lacks white bar on lesser coverts. Dark brown lessers, blackish at rear edge, contrast with pale grey medians and greaters (partly obscured by cinnamon fringes when fresh). Greaters narrowly tipped black and white. Also yellow on bill may be less extensive.

AGEING   Very difficult due to variable breeding season and rapid wear but sometimes by:

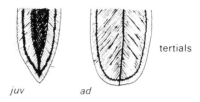

juv   ad   tertials

Coverts and tertials

Juv   All medians and tertials with distinct buff fringes, tertials pointed.

Ad   (And apparently *IW*) have mixture of uniform and buff-bordered feathers, tertials more rounded.

Tail

Juv   When fresh show tail down, or later a clear break where this has been lost.

Primaries

Juv   Pointed, and appear to wear rapidly.

Ad   When fresh are rounded.

SEXING   No characters found.

GEOGRAPHICAL VARIATION   Two intergrading races, one extra-limital: *B.s. inornatus* (E. and N. Africa) and *B.s. senegalensis* (W. Africa). Difficult to separate but the latter tends to have shorter wing.

BIOMETRICS   Sexes and ages combined.

		B.s. inornatus				*B.s. senegalensis*	
Wing	24 FG	208-231	(221.4)	:	25 FG	203-222	(213.8)
Bill	25 FG	39-45	(42.1)	:	24 FG	39-45	(41.0)
Tarsus	25 FG	68-77	(71.2)	:	25 FG	67-78	(72.4)

SPOTTED THICK-KNEE   *Burhinus capensis*

Marginal SC P (Arabia). Resident or short-distance migrant (E).

IDENTIFICATION   Similar to *B. oedicnemus* and *B. senegalensis* but lacking white on coverts, and with upperparts thickly mottled buff and brown rather than streaked. Greaters almost uniform grey. Underparts heavily streaked, especially breast.

GREAT STONE PLOVER   *Esacus recurvirostris*

Marginal SC P (Persian Gulf coasts). Mainly resident (O).

IDENTIFICATION   Like an outsize unstreaked *Burhinus*, but with very large bill with both mandibles angled up. Upperparts brownish-grey, underparts white with pale brown-grey breast. Black surrounding eye; white supercilium. Inner primaries extensively white, white bar across outer primaries; narrow black and white at tips of lesser coverts and tail. Bill yellow at base and black distally, iris yellow, legs greenish-grey.

EGYPTIAN PLOVER   *Pluvianus aegyptius*

SC P. Resident or short-distance migrant (E).

IDENTIFICATION   Smallish strikingly-patterned plover-like bird, with short stout black bill and blue-grey legs. Mainly grey above and creamy-buff below, but with black cap, eyestripe, back and narrow breastband. All black areas glossed green in post-juveniles. White supercilia meeting on nape. Tail tipped white, with narrow black subterminal band on outer feathers. Coverts grey, greaters tipped white. Remiges mainly white, with black wingbar and black leading and trailing edges to primaries.

AGEING

Ad   All year as above.

Juv   Leading lesser and median coverts and rump feathers rusty-brown. Head with rusty-brown feathers mixed with black. Breastband dull and thin. Once the rusty lessers have been lost they cannot be aged for certain. There are usually two groups separable on primary wear; those worn are likely to be *IY* and those fresh *Ad*, but as the breeding season varies locally so will the timing of wear. In NE Africa breeding is in early spring so wear is the only character after summer.

SEXING   No characters found.

BIOMETRICS

Wing	18 A♂	130-143	(135.1)	:	9 J	130-137	(133.7)
	16 A♀	127-143	(136.5)	:			
Bill	42 A	16-19	(17.5)	:	9 J	16-18	(17.0)
Tarsus	43 A	33-36	(34.4)	:	9 J	33-36	(34.3)

43

CREAM-COLOURED COURSER   *Cursorius cursor*

SW and SC P. Resident or short-distance migrant (E, O).

IDENTIFICATION   Tall creamy wader with a rather broad down-curved bill and long pale yellow legs. Axillaries and underwing entirely jet-black except for white trailing edge to secondaries. Outer half of upperwing black, inner half and rest of upperparts rich creamy. Underparts paler and greyer, especially on breast. White supercilia from behind eye meeting in V on grey nape, bordered below by black. Tail feathers except central pair tipped white and with black subterminal bar.

AGEING

Ad   Coverts uniform sandy-cream. Clear white supercilia. Primaries black although innermost may have small white fringes.

Juv   Upperparts sandy but strongly barred/mottled brown. Supercilia poorly marked, creamy-white above brownish eyestripe. Primaries black but all have broad creamy-buff tips. Breast with brown spotting.

IW   The brown bars wear rapidly and feathers are replaced quickly, then as *Ad* but told by combination of moult and retained buff-tipped primaries. *Juv* primaries wear rapidly but buff tips can still be seen on inners and middle. In early winter inner primaries moulted and *Ad* type gained—then can be aged on pattern of contrasting new black inners, moderately worn middle primaries with some buff tips, and very worn palish outers (the buff of which has worn off). In late winter *IW* can be difficult to distinguish from *Ad*, as the latter also have an apparently complex moult, but *Ad* usually has fresher and darker primaries.

SEXING   ♂ averages slightly larger than ♀.

GEOGRAPHICAL VARIATION   Three Palaearctic races: *C.c. exsul* (Cape Verde Is.), *C.c. cursor* (N. Africa-Iraq), and *C.c. bogolubovi* (Iran-India). In colour these grade from dark sandy to sandy/cream to pale greyish-sandy, and in size from smallest (wing 145-165) to largest (wing 160-175, bill 23-27), with *cursor* in between. Two extralimital races in E. Africa, *somaliensis* and *littoralis*, are both very small (7 *Ad* mean wing 138.7).

BIOMETRICS   *C.c. cursor*

Wing	14 A♂	160-172	(165.2)	:	11 J♂	155-170	(161.4)
	10 A♀	155-168	(162.4)	:	12 J♀	153-166	(160.5)
Bill*	37 A	21-25	(22.8)	:	30 J	20-24	(21.8)
Tarsus	39 A	52-63	(56.3)	:	30 J	51-61	(55.0)

*Measurements given are exposed culmen, excluding base which is hidden by forward-growing feathers.

44

PRATINCOLE   *Glareola pratincola*

SW and SC P. Resident or short- to medium-distance migrant (E).

IDENTIFICATION   Mainly brown wader with remarkable long pointed wings and deeply forked tail. Rump white, tail white with black tip. Underparts pale creamy with brownish breast. No collar, but creamy throat usually outlined in black. Short brownish-black legs. Bill stubby and broad at base, black with extensive red on gape in post-juveniles. Major distinctions from other pratincoles (which see):

	G. pratincola	G. maldivarum	G. nordmanni
underwing colour . . .	red	red	black
trailing edge of secondaries	white	dark	dark
Depth of tail-fork (inner/outer tail)			
Post juvenile	48-69	17-33	39-55
Juvenile	29-35	8-19	23-36

The white trailing edge to secondaries is rarely almost absent through wear. Red on gape is the most extensive of the three species, usually extending from nares to beneath base of lower mandible. Brown mantle and coverts contrast with dark brown primaries. Claw of middle toe 10-12mm, narrow at base and almost straight.

G. nordmanni

G. pratincola   claws

AGEING   A difficult species.

Ad SP   Upperparts and coverts brown. Head with thin black line around pale creamy throat. No contrasting old inner and new outer secondaries although usually with relatively worn inner primaries due to suspension of moult in autumn.

WP   During autumn and winter primary moult they have streaked head and throat and very thin pale tips to feathers of upperparts, but worn primaries provide distinction from *Juv*. Later as *SP* but slightly less well defined, with some streaking on head. Tips of secondaries of fairly uniform colour although outers often more worn than inners.

Juv   Upperparts, wings and tail brown with extensive buff tips and dark subterminal bands. Head and throat heavily streaked brown and buff. Tail-fork shallower than in *Ad*. Moult inner primaries and suspend while in full *Juv* plumage. Once body moult starts, primary moult completed almost immediately.

IW Once primary moult is complete can only be told by retained *Juv* inner secondaries, with slight buff tips and dark subterminal bars, contrasting with dark new white-tipped outer secondaries. Sometimes a few *Juv* tail feathers are retained for some months.

IS Attain *SP*, and only some can be identified by very worn inner secondaries contrasting with slightly worn outers.

SEXING *SP* ♂ Lores black, ♀ lores olive-brown.

size Tail-fork averages deeper in ♂.

GEOGRAPHICAL VARIATION Only one race, *G.p. pratincola* (Mediterranean-Iraq), in Palaearctic, told from two races S. of Sahara, *G.p. fuelleborni* and *G.p. limbata*, by having outer secondaries and inner primaries paler brown than other remiges giving a contrasting wing pattern. The extralimital races are darker and more closely resemble *G. nordmanni* and *G. maldivarum* in this character. African birds have less extensive red on underwing coverts and it may be admixed with some blackish-brown.

BIOMETRICS *G.p. pratincola*

Wing	24 A♂	185-203	(195.6)	:	6 J	178-199	(187.7)
	12 A♀	190-200	(195.0)	:			
Bill†	15 A	14-15	(14.5)	:	4 J	13-14	(13.7)
Tarsus	14 A	31-33	(31.6)	:	4 J	30-32	(31.0)
Tail diff.	24 FG♂	52-69	(58.3)	:	3*J	29-35	(33.0)
	12 FG♀	50-60	(55.0)	:			

† exposed culmen, excluding base which is concealed by forward-growing feathers.

* only autumn juv included.

REFERENCES (All pratincole species). Identification 54, 163, General 142.

EASTERN PRATINCOLE   *Glareola maldivarum*

SE P. Short- or medium-distance migrant (O).

IDENTIFICATION See *G. pratincola*. Remiges uniformly blackish-brown, as *G. nordmanni*. Underwing coverts red. Extent of red on gape and leg-length intermediate, but much shorter tail-difference than either species. Legs reported as reddish-cinnamon. Claw similar to *G. pratincola* but averaging slightly shorter.

AGEING As *G. pratincola*, but like *G. nordmanni* the retained buff-tipped *Juv* inner secondaries are distinctive throughout *IW* and into *IS*.

SEXING No plumage characters found, but perhaps as similar species. Tail-fork averages deeper in ♂.

BIOMETRICS

Wing	18 A♂	182-200	(190.8)	:	16 J	170-197	(184.6)	
	9 A♀	185-199	(190.0)	:				
Bill †	12 A	13-15	(14.2)	:	12 J	12-14	(13.2)	
Tarsus	13 A	32-37	(33.5)	:	11 J	30-35	(33.5)	
Tail diff.	17 A♂	22-33	(26.4)	:	6*J♂	14-25	(19.8)	
	9 A♀	17-30	(24.4)	:	5*J♀	8-19	(14.4)	

† exposed culmen, excluding base concealed by forward-growing feathers.
* only birds before post-juvenile tail moult included.

BLACK-WINGED PRATINCOLE *Glareola nordmanni*

MC P. Long-distance migrant.

IDENTIFICATION Similar to other species but always told by black underwing coverts and axillaries, and lack of white trailing edge to secondaries. Bill with red restricted to line along gape flanges starting from behind nares. Upperparts and coverts uniform dark brown with little or no contrast with primaries or secondaries helps to separate from *G.p. pratincola*. Longest-legged species, but tail-difference intermediate. Claw of middle toe 6-7mm, curved, and broad at base. Always with black on lores in *SP*, extensively in ♂.

juv   worn juv   ad and renewed *IW*

secondaries

AGEING Plumage sequence as *G. pratincola* but because the inner *Juv* secondaries (which are retained after primary and outer secondary moult in autumn) have characteristic buff tips and dark subterminal bands, they contrast clearly with the uniformly dark, unworn replaced remiges, throughout the *IW*. *IS* also told by this character.

SEXING *SP* ♂ Lores extensively black—reaching from nares to above and behind the eye, including the upper half of eyering. ♀ Lores black but a much smaller patch.

size Much greater sexual dimorphism than the other species with ♂ larger than ♀.

47

BIOMETRICS

Wing	11 A♂	193-216	(203.1)	:	7 J♂	180-209	(193.0)
	10 A♀	187-206	(197.5)	:	7 J♀	183-191	(185.9)
Bill †	17 A	12-15	(13.9)	:	11 J	12-15	(13.6)
Tarsus	18 A	35-41	(37.1)	:	10 J	34-39	(36.4)
Tail diff.	11 A♂	42-52	(47.7)	:	6*J♂	28-36	(31.0)
	11 A♀	39-53	(44.8)	:	6*J♀	23-31	(26.7)

†exposed culmen.
* only birds before post-juvenile tail-moult included.

LITTLE PRATINCOLE   *Glareola lactea*

Marginal SC P (Hindu Kush), resident or short-distance migrant (O).

IDENTIFICATION   Very small pratincole with upperparts pale greyish-brown, throat yellowish-buff without surrounding line, breast pale grey, and belly white. Coverts as mantle, remiges mainly black but with bold white bar across secondaries and sometimes a small white flash in middle primaries. Short forked tail, lacking streamers, white with black tips broadest on central feathers. Axillaries and underwing coverts black, contrasting strongly with white undersides to secondaries and inner primaries. Bill small, black with red at base. Legs brownish or greyish-black.

LITTLE RINGED PLOVER   *Charadrius dubius*

M and S P. Medium- to long-distance migrant (O, A).

IDENTIFICATION   Small plover, brown above and white below with white collar around neck. Breastband, mask and frontal bar brown, or blackish-brown/black in full plumage. Primaries brown with shaft of outer whitish. No wingbar, but primary and greater coverts narrowly tipped white, and narrow white trailing edge to inner secondaries. Tail squarish with white tip broader towards outer feathers, and with blackish-brown subterminal band broadest in centre. Outer feathers extensively white but with subterminal band extending across inner web. Legs dull flesh, sometimes yellowish. Bill entirely blackish or with small yellowish base to lower mandible. Bold yellow eyering, duller in immatures.

AGEING

Ad SP Coverts worn, fairly uniform sandy-grey with no fringes. Breastband black, often with some brown feathers.

WP Coverts as *SP;* when fresh sometimes with narrow white fringes, but these wear rapidly. Breastband brown although some birds, especially after midwinter, have mixture of black and brown. Moult July-November: primaries fresh in midwinter, slightly worn in spring.

Juv Upperparts sandy-brown with extensive buff fringes (redder on lesser coverts) and faint dark subterminal bands. Breastband brown, obscured and sometimes incomplete. Very obscure brown head-markings. Tail feathers with buff tips.

IW As *Ad WP* but buff-tipped *Juv* inner medians retained through winter; by late winter they are very difficult to see in some individuals. Primaries slightly worn in midwinter, moderately worn by spring.

IS Best told by very worn primaries although some individuals may retain *Juv* inner medians and other body feathers. Many have large number of brown feathers in black breastband.

SEXING *Ad SP* ♀ tends to have more brown in black head and breast patterns than ♂.

GEOGRAPHICAL VARIATION . Three races recognized, but only one in region: *C.d. curonicus* (Europe-Japan). Extralimital are *C.d. jerdoni* (SE Asia-India) and *C.d. dubius* (SE Asia-New Guinea). The Palaearctic race differs in having very little yellow at base of bill in *SP*, while *jerdoni* has much reduced black frontal bar. *Curonicus* has wing mean 116, bill 11-14; *jerdoni* is smaller with wing 110, bill 11-12; and nominate *dubius* larger, wing 116, bill 14-16.

BIOMETRICS: *C.d. curonicus*

Wing	36 A♂	112-120	(116.7)	:	6 J♂	114-120	(116.3)
	13 A♀	112-123	(117.8)	:	14 J♀	110-121	(114.9)
Bill	59 A	11-14	(13.4)	:	36 J	11-14	(13.2)
Tarsus	65 A	22-26	(24.4)	:	34 J	23-26	(24.5)

REFERENCES Moult 41, 76, Biometrics, Weight 11, 130.

RINGED PLOVER *Charadrius hiaticula*

N and MW P, NE N and rarely NW N. Resident or short- medium- or long-distance migrant.

IDENTIFICATION Smallish plover, in all plumages from *C. dubius* by larger size and clear white wingbar, and in *SP* by narrow orange eyering, lack of white above frontal bar, and usually broader blackish or black bands. In *SP* black of lores meets on forehead across base of bill. Bill in *SP* distinctly bicoloured, orange-yellow at base and black at tip; all blackish in *Juv*. Legs orange-yellow, duller in *Juv*. Outer tail feathers often wholly white, sometimes with blackish subterminal band across inner web. Usually one or two inner secondaries almost completely white. Only slight webbing between outer and middle toes. See *C. semipalmatus*, with which it interbreeds. *See Plate 1.*

AGEING

Ad SP Breastband and head pattern black, sometimes with a few brown feathers. Coverts grey-brown with thin pale whitish fringes. Bill orange-yellow with black tip. Legs bright orange-yellow.

WP Primary moult very variable depending on populations. Most Atlantic (i.e. western) breeders moult July-October, often with a suspension. N. Scandinavian and USSR (i.e. eastern) breeders start later; some begin October, suspend, and complete February-April, while others moult in winter without suspending. During moult and early winter breastband and mask are brownish, but black is regained in midwinter. Coverts grey-brown with whitish fringes on inners, but outers uniform. Bill dusky yellow at base, with black tip.

Juv Breastband brown, often reduced to lateral patches only just joining in centre. Head-markings brown, obscure. Upperparts and coverts very extensively fringed pale buff with dark subterminal bars. Bill blackish with a little yellow on base of lower mandible. Legs dull orange-yellow.

IW As *Ad WP* but some buff-tipped *Juv* inner medians are retained. Bill with base slightly yellowish. Primaries usually noticeably pointed. Pattern of primary wear varies, depending on moult. Western immatures have primaries slightly worn in winter, moderately worn by spring, and rarely moult in *IW*. Eastern immatures have a complete primary moult which may start as early as December and complete at the same time as *Ad;* these birds lose *Juv* coverts. In spring it is only possible to age eastern birds if contrast is visible where *Ad* suspended moult, i.e. division between oldish inner and fresh outer primaries. If no contrast, bird could be either *Ad* or *IW*.

IS Western birds by moderately worn primaries and sometimes by retained coverts. Usually attain black bands. Eastern birds appear unageable.

SEXING

Ad SP (May-September) Breastband: ♂ all black or with very few (<6%) brown feathers at the sides of the band, ♀ with considerable number (24-75%). This separates c85% of birds and might be useful even in *WP*. ♂ narrow orange eyering, ♀ dull grey eyering although often slightly yellowish.

size (per R. Taylor) ♂ averages slightly larger than ♀ in bill and tarsus but great overlap.

GEOGRAPHICAL VARIATION Two races generally accepted, *C.h. hiaticula* (NE Canada, Greenland, Iceland, S & W Europe) and *C.h. tundrae* (N. Fenno-Scandia, USSR), but distinctions are unclear. Typically, nominate *hiaticula* is larger and paler while *tundrae* is small and dark. There is however a cline of decreasing size from Britain to the north-east and it is very difficult to decide where (or even if) *tundrae* starts. To the north-west of Britain birds are also smaller, but not as small as *tundrae*; the only consistent difference within this sector is in the Icelandic breeders, which have short tarsi.

50

BIOMETRICS The sample sizes, ranges and means of three basic groups are set out below:

		Britain	Greenland	N Scand./USSR
Wing	Ad	45; 130-142 (135.3) :	36 ; 127-139 (131.9) :	54 ; 122-135 (128.9)
	Juv	9; 127-137 (133.6) :	3 ; 127-135 (130.7) :	26 ; 120-130 (126.3)
Bill	All	118; 13-16 (14.4) :	32 ; 12-15 (13.7) :	78 ; 13-15 (13.8)
Tarsus	All	100; 22-27 (25.0) :	35 ; 24-27 (25.4) :	100 ; 24-27 (25.3)

REFERENCES Age 41, Moult 6, 41, 76, 120, Sex 144, Variation 137B, 156, Biometrics 24, 44B, 94, 156, Weight 24, 44B, 92, 94.

SEMIPALMATED PLOVER *Charadrius semipalmatus*

N N. Medium- to long-distance migrant.

IDENTIFICATION Smallish plover, very like the smaller darker populations of *C. hiaticula* (with which it is sometimes considered conspecific), but with sizeable webbing between outer and middle toes and slight web, reaching the first joint, between inner and middle toes. Wingbar is slightly narrower and shorter than in *C. hiaticula*, and inner secondaries are darker, usually with inner webs entirely brown. In *SP* black collar tends to be narrower and more rounded, and the white patch behind and above the eye is often smaller than in *C. hiaticula*, and sometimes almost absent. Some interbreeding with *C. hiaticula* occurs in NE Canada.

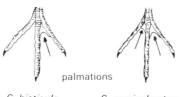

palmations

C. hiaticula   C. semipalmatus

AGEING

Ad SP Breastband and mask blackish, coverts brown and worn. Bill yellow with black tip.

WP Breastband and mask brown; coverts fresh, uniform brown or with very thin whitish fringes. Bill dull yellow with black tip. Primary moult is variable but usually late August-December, with some continuing into midwinter; primaries are fresh in midwinter, slightly worn in spring.

Juv Breastband brown. Coverts and back with extensive buff fringes and darker subterminal bands. Bill blackish.

IW As *Ad WP* but with some buff-tipped inner medians retained. Bill blackish. Primaries slightly worn in midwinter, moderately worn by spring.

IS Only by very worn primaries; usually moult before *Ad*, from June-September.

SEXING
Ad SP ♂ Breastband black with very few brown feathers; ♀ black with considerable number of brown feathers.

size ♀ averages fractionally larger.

GEOGRAPHICAL VARIATION General decrease in size from east (Hudson Bay) to west (Alaska), especially in winglength: *Ad* ♂ means approx. 128-121 and *Ad* ♀ 126-123 (per R. Taylor).

BIOMETRICS
Wing	28 A♂	118-131	(123.2)	: 16 J♂	114-123	(119.1)
	32 A♀	118-129	(124.3)	: 30 J♀	113-126	(120.5)
Bill	85 A	11-14	(12.6)	: 63 J	11-14	(12.3)
Tarsus	85 A	22-26	(24.1)	: 63 J	23-26	(23.9)

REFERENCES Biometrics 168, Weight 86, 97B, Variation 137B.

LONG-BILLED RINGED PLOVER *Charadrius placidus*

ME and SE P. Short-distance migrant.

IDENTIFICATION Medium-sized plover, fairly similar to *C. hiaticula* but larger, with no clear wingbar, and bill proportionately longer and more slender. In *SP* brownish or blackish mask often indistinct and dark of lores not meeting above bill. Frontal bar rather broader than *C. hiaticula,* and further distinguished by longish graduated tail with blackish subterminal band on outer feather extending to the outer web. In *SP* bill black with a small orange-yellow patch on base of lower mandible. Legs yellowish, duller than *C. hiaticula.* No wingbar on flight feathers but greater coverts tipped white and narrow white trailing edge to inner secondaries, recalling *C. dubius.*

C. semipalmatus   C. hiaticula   C. placidus

AGEING A difficult species to age, only told by:

Coverts Ad warm grey-brown with bright cinnamon tips in fresh plumage, wearing to uniform grey-brown.

Plate 1 OYSTERCATCHER: JUVENILE. *Note for ageing no neck collar, very dark pointed bill, very dark eye and traces of buff on coverts.*

RINGED PLOVER: JUVENILE. *Young juvenile with brown breastband almost incomplete, and no black on head pattern. Distinct dark subterminal lines inside pale buff fringes to mantle, but these are less distinct on coverts.*

Plate 2 DOTTEREL: JUVENILE. *Easily identified by shape, pale line on breast and bold supercilium. Coverts, scapulars and tertials with pale buff fringes, interrupted at tip by dark central mark, indicate a juvenile.*

LESSER GOLDEN PLOVER: JUVENILE. *Note pale (yellow/gold) spots and especially dark brown bars on almost all of underparts. Superficial resemblance to juvenile Grey Plover (see Plate 3).*

Plate 3 GREY PLOVER: JUVENILE. *Note coverts and tertials, scapulars and mantle with many distinctive pale (yellowish) spots. Underparts with extensive darker shaft streaks and paler brown tips to feathers.*

SANDERLING: JUVENILE. *Note paired whitish spots, clearest on scapulars and tertials. On some coverts the thin black terminal line can be seen. Juveniles also characteristically have a much darker back than adults, which in autumn are rapidly gaining pale grey winter plumage.*

Plate 4 KNOT: JUVENILE. *The picture shows brownish-grey mantle, scapulars and coverts with very obvious dark subterminal bands and whitish edgings.*

CURLEW SANDPIPER: JUVENILE. *Note longish legs and bill and slim shape, also pale largely unstreaked breast. The clear buff fringes to grey-brown juvenile coverts are distinctive.*

Plate 5 DUNLIN: ADULT SUMMER PLUMAGE. *Note mixture of dark (chestnut) and pale (whitish) edgings to dark mantle, this with small black belly suggests a southern European type. The relatively dark nape (with little grey) indicates, in W. Palaearctic populations, that it is a female.*

DUNLIN: JUVENILE MOULTING INTO IW PLUMAGE. *A mixture of typical juvenile coverts with grey-brown centres and distinct buff fringes, and replaced adult-type coverts and scapulars which are uniform grey with darker shaft streaks, paling towards edges. Also remaining but being replaced are dark spots on upper belly which are characteristic of juveniles.*

Plate 6 PURPLE SANDPIPER: ADULT, WINTER. *Most coverts are uniform dark slate grey, paler towards edges. This pattern is typical of adult and replaced first winter coverts in all* Calidris *sandpipers. Fresh primaries indicate that this is an adult.*

PECTORAL SANDPIPER: JUVENILES. *These show distinct pale (whitish-buff) fringes to mantle, scapulars, tertials and coverts, and whitish lines on mantle. Distinct pectoral band and fairly strong fine streaking all over breast distinguishes easily from Sharp-tailed Sandpiper.*

Plate 7 BROAD-BILLED SANDPIPER: ADULT, SUMMER. *Note very dark mantle, worn coverts, fairly darkly spotted breast, white belly and double supercilium. In all plumages has short legs and a distinctively drooped tip to the upper mandible.*

BUFF-BREASTED SANDPIPER: JUVENILE. *A very distinctive species with buff face and underparts and scaly upperparts. Only juveniles have dark subterminal spots on coverts inside terminal whitish-buff fringe, and blackish scapulars with whitish fringes.*

Plate 8 BLACK-TAILED GODWIT: JUVENILE. *Evenly-fringed mantle and coverts indicate that this bird is a fresh juvenile. Neck is pale cinnamon; coverts are strongly fringed reddish-buff.*

BAR-TAILED GODWIT: FIRST WINTER (DECEMBER). *This bird retains many juvenile coverts with worn but still extensive pale buff sides to feathers. Mantle feathers are replaced adult type. Of the three tertials visible the uppermost is replaced adult type (unworn) while the two lower are worn juvenile feathers with strong pale and dark bars.*

Juv As *Ad* but fringed pale buff. These are rapidly lost in autumn and replaced by *Ad* type. Contrast between pale fringes of inners and bright fringes of other coverts in autumn indicates *Juv*.

Primary Wear Ad moult July-September, rarely later, so primaries are fresh in midwinter, slightly worn in spring and moderately worn in summer.

IW Primaries are slightly worn in early winter, fairly worn in later winter, and moderately worn in spring. *IS* only by very worn primaries.

SEXING No characters found.

BIOMETRICS (Ages combined).

Wing	23♂	135-152	(142.9)	: 27♀	135-154	(143.5)
Bill	22♂	19-21	(19.9)	: 27♀	18-21	(19.8)
Tarsus	23♂	30-34	(32.0)	: 28♀	30-34	(32.1)

WILSON'S PLOVER *Charadrius wilsonia*

Coastal S N. Resident or short- to medium-distance migrant (N).

IDENTIFICATION Small to medium-sized plover, told from other ringed plovers by long and heavy black bill forming a strong line with black, rufous or brown mask, and by rather broad breastband. Clear white forehead is continuous with short white supercilium. White wingbar. Squarish white-fringed tail with dark subterminal bar, outer rectrices extensively white with brownish subterminal marks on inner web. Rufous breastband in some *SP* females is distinctive. Legs dull flesh-pink.

AGEING

Ad SP Breastband and frontal bar black or dark brown.

WP Breastband and frontal bar palish brown and the latter much less distinct. Coverts grey-brown, slightly paler towards tip. Moult June-October, so primaries fresh in winter and slightly worn in spring.

Juv Brown breastband and frontal bar very pale and indistinct. Coverts and mantle feathers with broad buff fringes and dark subterminal bands.

IW Bands remain pale brown. Buff fringes on coverts abrade rapidly but faint buff edges remain on inner medians throughout winter. Primaries slightly worn in winter, moderately worn in spring.

IS Less black or dark brown in bands than *Ad*. Coverts very worn; plumage generally worn and pale. Primaries worn.

SEXING Only in *Ad SP* by forehead and breastband: *Ad♂* black, with just occasional brown feathers, *Ad♀* warm brown (see below).

GEOGRAPHICAL VARIATION Two races described in region, *C.w. wilsonia* (east U.S.A.) and *C.w. beldingi* (south-west U.S.A.—Mexico). Nominate *wilsonia* is more black and brown, while *beldingi* ♂ has rufous tinge to crown and ♀ has bright rufous breastband.

BIOMETRICS

Wing	27 A♂	116-126	(122.2)	:	8 J	116-122	(118.0)
	25 A♀	117-128	(122.6)	:			
Bill	52 A	19-22	(20.9)	:	8 J	20-22	(20.5)
Tarsus	52 A	28-32	(30.0)	:	8 J	28-30	(29.4)

KILLDEER   *Charadrius vociferus*

M and S N. Medium- to long-distance migrant (N).

IDENTIFICATION   Medium-sized to large plover, distinguished from other ringed plovers by larger size, two black breastbands in all plumages, and boldly-patterned rump and tail. Broad and long white wingbar. Rufous fringes to upperparts in fresh plumage. Rump and upper tail coverts bright orange; tail recalling *C. placidus* but proportionately longer and more graduated with white tip, black subterminal band, and some orange-brown at base. Bill black, legs dull yellowish or flesh.

AGEING

Ad   In fresh plumage mantle and coverts extensively fringed rich rufous and buffish-brown. In winter outer coverts abrade and uniform rufous fringes remain on inner medians only. Moult July-October, so primaries fresh in winter and slightly worn in spring.

Juv   As *Ad* once fledged but mantle and coverts with buff fringes and darkish indistinct subterminal marks. Tail with long down streamers often retained for several weeks, and when streamers have been lost the breakage zone is usually distinct.

IW   As *Ad* but some scapulars and buff-fringed inner medians are retained. The contrast with replaced rufous-fringed outer coverts is very difficult to see by midwinter. Most of tail is replaced by winter, often with contrast of worn soft *Juv* and fresh *IW* feathers together. Primaries slightly worn in early winter, moderately worn by spring.

IS   Only by moderately worn primaries.

SEXING   No characters found although some ♀ have much brown admixed with black in the face-pattern.

GEOGRAPHICAL VARIATION   Only one race in region, nominate *vociferus*, but two more in the Neotropics.

BIOMETRICS

Wing	16 A♂	160-173	(166.9)	:	31 J♂	156-172	(163.6)
	14 A♀	159-175	(169.4)	:	13 J♀	158-173	(166.1)
Bill	16 A♂	19-21	(20.1)	:	30 J♂	18-22	(19.7)
	10 A♀	18-21	(19.7)	:	15 J♀	19-21	(20.1)
Tarsus	17 A♂	33-38	(36.1)	:	32 J♂	33-38	(35.8)
	15 A♀	33-37	(35.4)	:	14 J♀	33-37	(35.1)

PIPING PLOVER   *Charadrius melodus*

MC and ME·N. Short-to medium-distance migrant.

IDENTIFICATION Smallish plover, pale sandy-grey above and with blackish in *SP* restricted to narrow frontal bar, narrow sometimes incomplete breastband, and collar. Lores often white and ear-coverts pale sandy. Bold white wingbar. Longest upper tail coverts whitish forming a unique tail-pattern. Outer tail-feather completely white, or with small subterminal mark across inner web. Stubby bill, blackish, or in *SP* yellow or orangey with a black tip. Legs orange-yellow, duller in winter.

AGEING

Ad SP Black or blackish-brown frontal bar and complete or interrupted breastband. Upperparts and coverts uniform greyish-sandy colour. Underparts white. Bill yellow or orange with black tip.

WP Frontal bar lost and breastband reduced to lateral grey patches. Upperparts and coverts pale sandy-grey, latter at first with palish edges. Bill blackish. Moult September-February, so primaries are fresh in midwinter and slightly worn in summer.

Juv Upperparts and coverts sandy-grey broadly tipped pinkish-buff. Completely lacks black or brown frontal bar and breastband, the latter as in *Ad WP*. Bill as *Ad WP*.

IW As *Ad WP* but inner medians retain pale buff fringes until spring (when can be difficult to see). Primaries are slightly worn in midwinter, moderately worn in spring.

IS Only by moderately worn primaries. Attain *SP* but slightly paler than *Ad*.

SEXING *Ad SP* ♂ black, ♀ blackish-brown breastband and frontal bar. ♀ frequently has breastband reduced to lateral spots. Bill of ♂ more orange, of ♀ more yellow.

Ad WP Not sexable until *SP* starts to appear, sometimes as early as November when breastband colour may be useful.

IW Some ♂ identified if black is present in breastband, from midwinter.

GEOGRAPHICAL VARIATION Two races described, but great individual variation: nominate *melodus* (East coast) and *circumcinctus* (Great Lakes westwards). Former has breastband usually broken, but usually complete in *circumcinctus*.

BIOMETRICS

Wing	16 A♂	118-127	(122.3)	: 9 J	114-124	(120.6)
	6 A♀	118-127	(123.7)	:		
Bill	32 A	12-14	(12.8)	: 9 J	12-13	(12.7)
Tarsus	34 A	21-24	(22.6)	: 9 J	21-23	(22.3)

KITTLITZ'S PLOVER   *Charadrius pecuarius*

SC P. Mainly resident (E).

IDENTIFICATION   Small plover, greyish- or blackish-brown above, with breastband completely lacking. In *SP* has black or brownish-black frontal bar, also stripe through eye from bill to sides of neck. White supercilia from behind eye join on nape, and white also narrowly above the frontal bar. Underparts orange-buff paling towards belly and rear flanks, or brownish-buff in *WP* and *Juv*. Short wingbar formed by small white flash in inner primaries and narrow tips to outer greater coverts, and greyish-brown medians and greaters contrasting with blackish remiges and leading lessers give a unique wing-pattern. Tail progessively whiter towards sides, with outer 1-2 pairs completely white, and darker subterminal band on central feathers only. Bill and legs black or blackish, legs sometimes greenish-grey.

AGEING

Ad SP   Eyestripe black, extending from bill through eye. Frontal bar black. Coverts fairly uniform grey-brown. Underparts rich buff.

WP   As *SP* but black eyestripe becoming brown during later stages of moult (occasionally some black retained). Frontal bar absent. Underparts much paler buff. Collar whitish. Timing of primary moult appears to vary between localities (probably dependent on breeding season).

Juv   Upperparts, including coverts, brown broadly edged pale buff-brown. Blackish lesser coverts may be partly obscured at first. Lacks any dark facial markings although has indistinct pale supercilium. Underparts whitish tinged buffish-brown on breast.

IW   Buff-brown fringes lost and coverts have dull appearance, although some fringes are retained on inner medians. Collar whitish-buff.

IS   Variable in plumage but usually resemble dull *Ad SP* with less well-defined head markings; some do not attain *SP*. Often retain some *Juv* inner medians. Primaries tend to be more pointed and moderately worn.

SEXING   In *SP* : *Ad* ♂ tends to have black facial markings, ♀ duller with a little brown—to be used with extreme caution; ♂ with much richer coloured breast. ♀ tends to be heavier.

BIOMETRICS (from all Africa, but size is likely to vary locally).

Wing	31 A♂	99-112	(105.8)	:	6 J♂	98-106	(103.0)
	15 A♀	101-111	(105.1)	:	11 J♀	100-111	(103.5)
Bill	53 A	15-18	(16.1)	:	26 J	15-17	(15.7)
Tarsus	54 A	28-33	(30.4)	:	25 J	29-33	(30.6)

REFERENCES   Age 151.

KENTISH PLOVER   *Charadrius alexandrinus*

M and S H. Short- to medium-distance migrant (E, O, A, N).

IDENTIFICATION Small plover, with breastband always restricted to lateral patches and white of forehead always continuous with supercilium. In *SP* ♂, mask, frontal bar and breast patches are black or blackish and crown is sometimes rufous—these areas are brown in other plumages. In Nearctic birds upperparts are rather pale brown and the mask does not reach the bill. Clear white wingbar, and tail-feathers 4-6 completely white giving broad white sides to tail. Bill black, legs dark grey or blackish.

AGEING

Ad SP Breast patches either clear black or brown. Coverts grey-brown, edged paler. During autumn moult the new coverts have pale brown-washed edges; these can resemble *Juv* but the brown (not buff) forms a wash rather than a fringe.

WP Breast patches of both sexes become brown (see sexing). Coverts fade and wear fairly quickly leaving grey-brown feathers. Moult July-September, so primaries fresh in winter and slightly worn in spring.

Juv Breast patches pale brown, often indistinct. Upperparts and coverts grey-brown with distinct buff fringes.

IW As *Ad WP* but pale buff-fringed inner medians retained. Primaries slightly worn midwinter, moderately worn spring.

IS Often some retained inner medians. Primaries very worn. Many attain *SP*.

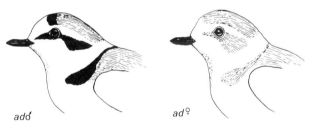

ad♂   *ad♀*

SEXING

Ad SP ♂ has black or brownish-black breast and head patches, ♀ brown but rarely with a few black feathers. *WP* ♂ with broader white collar and supercilium. On breastband black of ♂ may start to show as early as November/December.

IW Only for ♂ when black starts to show, from midwinter.

GEOGRAPHICAL VARIATION Worldwide distribution with many forms described. Principal northern ones are nominate *alexandrinus* (Europe, N. Africa to Korea), *dealbatus* (E. Asia, Japan) and *nivosus* (N. American Snowy Plover).

	colour-eye to bill	mantle colour	wing length	bill length	tarsus length
C.a. alexandrinus	black	grey-brown	105-120	14-17	25-30
C.a. dealbatus	black	grey-brown	109-123	16-19	25-30
C.a. nivosus	white	paler	<110	13-16	23-26

Main variation elsewhere in the world is in amount of rufous on crown and nape.

BIOMETRICS   *C.a. alexandrinus*

Wing	53 A♂	102-115	(111.4) :	27 J♂	102-116	(110.1)
	26 A♀	105-116	(111.8) :	36 J♀	105-115	(110.7)
Bill	59 A	14-17	(15.3) :	32 J	14-16	(15.1)
Tarsus	60 A	26-30	(28.0) :	34 J	25-30	(27.4)

REFERENCES   Moult 41, 76, 120, Biometrics 27, 117, 131, Weight 117, 131.

LESSER SANDPLOVER   *Charadrius mongolus*

SC, ME and NE P, also rarely NW N. Medium- to long-distance migrant.

IDENTIFICATION   Smallish plover, darkish brown above and mainly white below, lacking white collar around the nape. Distinctive broad pale chestnut-red breastband and chestnut on nape and supercilia in *SP;* underparts with indistinct lateral brownish smudges in winter. In *SP* black or blackish mask, forehead except for white lateral patches, and in some birds a narrow line above chestnut breastband. Wingbar short and narrow, formed by tips to greater coverts and white on outer webs of outer secondaries and primaries 1-5(6), also a narrow white trailing edge to secondaries. Tail fringed white, with outer feather whitish admixed pale brown. Underwing and sides to rump whitish. Bill black, legs grey or blackish. From *C. leschenaultii* in all plumages by smaller size and proportionately smaller and weaker bill, in *SP* by broader breastband and in *Juv* by brighter buff breast. Measurements see below:

		wing			bill length			tarsus	
C. mongolus	122 A	119-144	(130.5) :	15-20	(17.1) :		27-35 (31.6)	
	80 J	118-143	(127.1) :	15-20	(17.1) :		27-34 (31.6)	
C. leschenaultii								
	70 A	135-153	(145.0) :	20-27	(24.6) :		34-40 (36.7)	
	46 J	133-148	(140.5) :	21-26	(23.6) :		35-39 (37.0)	
In general	wing <140,		bill <20,	tarsus <34	is *C. mongolus*			
	wing >140,		bill >20,	tarsus >35	is *C. leschenaultii*			

Measurements separate all western birds but a very small percentage of eastern birds overlap. *See frontispiece.*

'mongolus' group   'atrifrons' group

C. mongolus   ad ♂ sp   C. leschenaultii

AGEING

AD SP Upperparts brown with rufous crown and nape. Black and white face pattern (variable with race), and broad reddish breastband separated from white throat by narrow black line (except south-western birds). Rest of underparts white.

WP Upperparts greyish-brown, coverts narrowly fringed white. Head with whitish frontal area and supercilium. Underparts white, with fairly large brown-grey lateral breast patches sometimes joining in centre. Moult August-October, so primaries are fresh in winter and slightly worn in spring.

Juv Upperparts and coverts extensively fringed buff, especially bright on scapulars. Head as *Ad WP*. Breast patches with greyish feathers edged buff on buffish background.

IW As *Ad WP* but buff-tipped inner medians retained. In Africa and W. Asia primaries are slightly worn in early winter, moderately worn by spring. In S.E. Asia appear to have full moult from late winter.

IS Primaries very worn or in S.E. Asia very fresh. Often remain south of breeding range and do not attain *SP*.

SEXING   Ad SP On average ♂ much brighter than ♀ but considerable variation and method is to be used with caution. Black in ♀ usually with some grey-brown.

GEOGRAPHICAL VARIATION   Four races in two groups. The south-western *atrifrons* group contains *pamirensis* (SC USSR) and *atrifrons* (Tibet-SW China), and north-eastern *mongolus* group consists of nominate *mongolus* (E USSR, Mongolia) and *stegmanni* (NE USSR). Clines of increasing size and darkness exist from south-west to north-east and it is very difficult to separate races. The two groups can be separated by:

	forehead	*breast*	*size*
atrifrons group	almost all black	no blackish line separating white throat/red breast	smaller
mongolus group	white bisected vertically by black line	blackish line present	larger

59

BIOMETRICS

C.m. atrifrons

Wing	41 A♂	119-132	(127.8)	:	9 J♂	118-136	(125.4)
	31 A♀	123-134	(128.8)	:	27 J♀	118-133	(124.3)
Bill	76 A	15-20	(17.4)	:	46 J	16-20	(17.5)
Tarsus	77 A	30-35	(32.4)	:	46 J	30-36	(32.4)

C.m. mongolus

Wing	21 A♂	127-145	(134.5)	:	13 J♂	125-136	(129.1)
	15 A♀	127-140	(134.8)	:	16 J♀	127-143	(130.6)
Bill	51 A	15-19	(16.6)	:	37 J	15-19	(16.5)
Tarsus	52 A	27-34	(30.6)	:	38 J	27-34	(30.7)

REFERENCES Moult 76, Biometrics, Weight 27.

GREATER SANDPLOVER *Charadrius leschenaultii*

SC and SE P. Medium- to long-distance migrant.

IDENTIFICATION Medium-sized plover, larger than *C. mongolus* (which see) and with proportionately larger and heavier bill with well-marked gonys. In *SP* narrower chestnut breastband, and sometimes with chestnut admixed on back and scapulars. More white in wings and tail than *C. mongolus*, with brownish on outer tail-feather usually restricted to a small subterminal area. Bill black; legs grey, sometimes fleshy or greenish or more yellowish than *C. mongolus*.

AGEING

Ad SP Upperparts and coverts warm brown with rufous nape. Striking head pattern with white frontal patch, black bar on forehead, narrow black line from bill to eye, and broad black post-orbital line. Narrow chestnut breastband, sometimes with trace of black upper margin. Rest of underparts white.

WP Upperparts brownish-grey, forehead and supercilium pale. All black lost. Breastband reduced to grey-brown lateral breast patches usually joining in a thin grey line across centre of breast. Coverts brownish-grey with narrow whitish fringe on inners. Underparts white. Moult July-September, so primaries are fresh in winter and slightly worn in spring.

Juv Upperparts and coverts brownish extensively fringed buff. Poorly marked head pattern, with no black, and indistinct supercilium. Breast patches grey-brown on buffish wash.

IW As *Ad WP* but buff-fringed inner medians retained. Primaries generally slightly worn in early winter and moderately worn in spring, but in SE Asia *IW* may have primary moult.

IS Very worn primaries in most cases; appear to attain some *SP*.

SEXING ♀ in *SP* often dull, with blackish-brown replacing black and with chestnut duller than in ♂, but can be bright.

BIOMETRICS

Wing	25 A♂	139-150	(144.8)	:	22 J♂	133-147	(140.3)
	39 A♀	135-153	(145.0)	:	16 J♀	134-148	(140.4)
Bill	76 A	20-28	(24.6)	:	45 J	21-26	(23.6)
Tarsus	71 A	34-40	(36.7)	:	46 J	35-39	(37.0)

REFERENCES Moult 76, Biometrics, Weight 27.

CASPIAN PLOVER *Charadrius asiaticus*

MC P. Long-distance migrant.

IDENTIFICATION Small to medium-sized plover resembling sandplovers, but with deep chestnut breastband in *SP* and usually complete brown breastband in winter. Poor wingbar formed by white tips to outer greater coverts and white on outer webs of primaries 1-4(5). No white on sides to rump and white on outer tail feather restricted to very narrow fringe and tip. From sandplovers in *SP* by lack of blackish and chestnut on head and by breastband usually blackish bordering the white belly, and in all plumages by less compact shape, weak bill and less white in wings and tail. Upperparts have clear rufous and buff fringes when fresh. From similar *C. veredus* by smaller size (wing ⩽ 158, tarsus ⩽42), usually well-defined whitish supercilium in *SP*, whitish underwing with axillaries suffused pale brown, and clear but small white wingbar. Bill black, legs dull greenish.

C. veredus   ado̓   C. asiaticus

AGEING

Ad SP Upperparts, including coverts, brown with many pink-buff fringes; fringes wear rapidly however. Throat white, breastband chestnut usually lined black below. Belly white.

61

WP Upperparts as *SP*. Coverts with all fringes initially a uniform pink-buff, mostly worn off by late autumn. Breastband grey-brown, belly white. Moult starts April/May, suspends July-October, and completes November/December; primaries are fresh in winter and only slightly worn in spring and summer.

Juv Upperparts brown with very extensive pink-buff edgings. Coverts with pale buff fringes on lessers and inner medians but some pink-buff fringes on outers. Breastband variably buff/grey-brown.

IW As *Ad WP* but coverts with contrasting pale buff inner medians and pink-buff outers. Primaries slightly worn in early winter, moderately worn in spring.

IS Only by very worn primaries, but a few retain *Juv* inner medians.

SEXING *SP* Little difference, but ♀ tends to have duller rufous breastband which lacks or has indistinct black lower band.

BIOMETRICS

Wing	20 A♂	141-157	(149.8)	:	23 J♂	140-155	(146.9)
	12 A♀	140-154	(146.7)	:	18 J♀	140-153	(145.3)
Bill	41 A	18-22	(20.2)	:	46 J	18-22	(20.1)
Tarsus	44 A	37-42	(39.7)	:	48 J	36-41	(39.1)

REFERENCES Moult 76.

ORIENTAL PLOVER *Charadrius veredus*

ME P. Long-distance migrant.

IDENTIFICATION Medium to large plover, similar to *C. asiaticus* but larger and proportionately longer-legged (wing usually ⩾ 160, tarsus ⩾ 43), with browner underwing and axillaries brown narrowly fringed white. Also lacks clear wingbar, but outer greater coverts narrowly tipped white and sometimes some white traces on outer webs of primaries 1-4. In *SP* often much whiter on head and neck, some birds completely whitish or creamy except for brown rear crown; supercilium always broad and poorly-defined, usually creamy. Bill black. Legs dull greenish, sometimes fleshy or yellowish.

AGEING

Ad SP For details see sexing. Upperparts brownish extensively fringed chestnut-buff. Coverts grey-brown with small rich buff fringes which wear off rapidly.

WP Upperparts and coverts as *SP*, rapidly becoming uniform. Underparts whitish with broad breastband, buffish-brown in ♀, pinkish-brown in ♂. Moult in summer, suspending briefly and completing by October/November, so primaries are fresh in winter and slightly worn in spring.

Juv Upperparts brown extensively fringed pale buff and pale chestnut. Coverts fringed pale buff. Throat whitish, breast mottled darkish brown/buff, belly white.

IW As *Ad WP* but pale buff-fringed inner median coverts contrast with chestnut-fringed replaced outers. Inner primaries edged whitish. Primaries slightly worn in midwinter, moderately worn in spring.

IS Sometimes retain inner medians but best told by very worn primaries. A dull *SP* breastband usually attained by ♂ (feathers pinkish-chestnut, fringed buff).

SEXING *SP Ad* ♂ Front of crown and neck very white at first. Throat white, breast grading from pale chestnut at throat to deep rich chestnut on lower breast, bordered by fairly broad black lower line. *Ad* ♀ Cap brown, neck pale brown only slightly contrasting with mantle. Throat pale buff, becoming darker brownish-buff on breast. Lacks black breastband.

BIOMETRICS All combined as few sexed specimens examined.

Wing	27 A	157-178	(169.1)	: 21 J	156-169	(163.0)
Bill	28 A	21-25	(22.9)	: 19 J	20-25	(22.6)
Tarsus	29 A	43-50	(46.2)	: 22 J	44-48	(45.6)

MOUNTAIN PLOVER   *Charadrius montanus*

MC and SC N. Short-distance migrant.

IDENTIFICATION Medium-sized plover, buffish-brown above and white below with buffish-brown breast patches. In *SP* black or blackish frontal bar and line joining eye and bill. In *WP* more extensively brownish below. Extensive rufous and buff fringes to upperparts when fresh. White underwing and axillaries usually contrasting strongly with brownish or buffish flanks. Narrow but clear white wingbar, tail white-fringed and with blackish subterminal band. Bill black, legs pale brownish-yellow.

AGEING

Ad SP Black or blackish frontal bar and line joining eye and bill.

WP Lacks black face markings. Uniform brownish-grey median coverts with distinctive rufous-brown fringes. Moult apparently August-October, so primaries fresh in winter and slightly worn in spring.

Juv Upperparts, including coverts, brownish-grey broadly tipped buffish with dark subterminal bands. No black face pattern.

IW Buff tips abrade quickly and subterminal bands are lost. Median coverts show contrast between inner buff *Juv* feathers and outer new *Ad* type with rufous-brown fringes. Primaries slightly more worn than *Ad*.

IS Usually attain *SP*, but some *Juv* inner medians are retained.

63

SEXING   No characters found.

BIOMETRICS   Sexes combined as few sexed specimens examined.

Wing	23 A	144-159	(152.9)	: 24 J	144-157	(149.1)
Bill	20 A	20-23	(21.2)	: 21 J	19-22	(20.7)
Tarsus	23 A	38-42	(40.1)	: 24 J	38-42	(39.8)

REFERENCES   Sex, Weight 43.

DOTTEREL   *Eudromias morinellus*

Discontinuous in N and M P, also extreme NW N. Medium- to long-distance migrant.

IDENTIFICATION   Medium-sized plover, always with narrow whitish breastband and bold white or whitish supercilia. Narrow wings without wingbar, tail white-fringed and with dark subterminal bar. Black and chestnut belly, grey breast, blackish crown and broad white supercilia distinctive in *SP*. Legs dull yellow. Small blackish bill sometimes tinged greenish at base of lower mandible. *See Plate 2.*

AGEING

Ad SP   Cap dark, supercilium white. Back and coverts sandy-brown with broad sandy/cinnamon edges. Greyish upper breast, with white line at lower edge; upper belly chestnut, lower belly black, vent and under tail coverts white.

WP   Upperparts similar to but paler than *SP*. Coverts as *SP*. Breast grey-brown crossed by whitish line, belly white. Moult starts July/August, suspends on or near breeding grounds, restarts on wintering grounds December/January and is completed by end February/early March. There is a contrast of new inners and old outers in winter, but all primaries are fresh in spring.

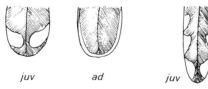

juv   ad   juv   ad

inner median coverts   tertials

Juv   Back, coverts, scapulars and tertials dark brown with broad buff fringes interrupted by central dark wedge to tip of feathers. Breast brownish-buff, with indistinct white line, and belly white.

IW   Like pale *Juv*. Coverts, especially inners, with distinctive dark brown central area. Primaries moderately worn by January/February.

IS   Some *Juv* inner medians retained; primaries very worn. Usually attain *SP*, then moult as *Ad*.

SEXING Only *Ad* in *SP* sexable and then only safely when in breeding pairs. Typically *Ad♀* with darker, more uniformly blackish cap, brighter white supercilium, clearer grey on upper breast, and larger and more solid area of black on belly. Sometimes ♂ may show these characters, but dull birds are almost always ♂. ♂ has brood patch.

BIOMETRICS

Wing	23 A♂	143-163	(150.8)	:	18 J♂	145-163	(151.7)
	13 A♀	148-162	(155.5)	:	15 J♀	147-163	(155.0)
Bill	46 A	15-19	(16.5)	:	41 J	15-18	(16.4)
Tarsus	47 A	34-40	(36.9)	:	42 J	34-40	(37.0)

REFERENCES Moult 76, Sex 99, Weight 43.

LESSER GOLDEN PLOVER   *Pluvialis dominica*

NC and NE P, N N. Long-distance migrant.

IDENTIFICATION Largish plover resembling *P. apricaria*, and in non-breeding plumages also *E. morinellus*. From *E. morinellus* by larger black bill, dull greyish legs, no whitish breastband, uniformly dark tail, larger size, and indistinct wingbar formed by white on primary shafts only. Smaller than *P. apricaria* but with proportionately longer bill and legs, and told in all plumages by fulvous-grey underwing and axillaries. In *SP* black on underparts is more extensive than in *P. apricaria*, and in full plumage undertail coverts are black not white. In non-breeding plumages *P.d. dominica* is greyer than *P. apricaria* while *P.d. fulva* is frequently more buff, and both have a clearer supercilium. *See Plate 2.*

AGEING

Juv/IW Brown-tipped white feathers on flanks and belly are distinctive; the tips wear off but are clear to December and some are usually retained in flanks to March.

Combination of degree of *Ad SP* and primary wear is of considerable help in ageing and is summarised below.

	July-Sept	*Oct-Dec*	*Jan-Feb*	*March-June*
Juv	1° new	1° slightly worn	1° moderately worn	1° very worn
Ad (fulva)	1° worn, inners suspending	active moult	new or completing	1° fairly new
Ad (dominica)	1° worn, no moult present	active moult	new or completing	1° fairly new
Summer plumage (black belly)		lost in October	winter plumage	*Ad*–complete by April. *IS*–partial May

65

SEXING Only possible for *Ad* in *SP*. ♂ underparts uniform black (*P.d. dominica*) or brownish-black (*P.d. fulva*); ♀ with a variable, usually fairly small, number of whitish feathers in black underparts—especially on lower belly and under tail coverts. In *P.d. dominica IS* ♂ resembles *Ad*♀ but tends to have more white.

GEOGRAPHICAL VARIATION Two races, nominate *dominica* (N. America—E. USSR) and *fulva* (USSR—Alaska). The two races are fairly similar but told in *Ad WP* and *IW* by *dominica* having a brownish-grey background colour on breast and duller yellow on head and neck, while *fulva* has breast with a fairly bright yellow-buff background colour, relatively bright yellow-buff on head and brighter gold on back. *Ad* in *SP* difficult to separate but *fulva* with brighter gold spotting on back, and *dominica* tends to show more white especially on forehead and sides of breast.

Juv dominica has very extensive brown tips to almost whole of underparts; in *fulva* these are less extensive, mainly on breast and flanks.

Winglength provides good separation although the overlapping *dominica* and largest *fulva* occur together in Alaska:

		Typical		*Alaska*		*Typical*
P.d. dominica	A	173-188	:	176-193	:	J 169-187
P.d. fulva	A	152-173	:	164-180	:	J 154-171

BIOMETRICS *P.d. dominica*

Wing	21 A♂	173-193	(182.5)	:	7 J♂	175-185	(180.4)
	19 A♀	175-188	(182.5)	:	13 J♀	169-187	(177.8)
Bill	54 A	20-27	(23.1)	:	29 J	21-25	(22.7)
Tarsus	56 A	39-44	(41.4)	:	28 J	39-43	(41.6)

P.d. fulva (no sexed Alaskan birds examined, so see above)

Wing	32 A♂	157-173	(163.7)	:	14 J♂	154-171	(164.4)
	28 A♀	152-168	(162.1)	:	18 J♀	160-169	(164.3)
Bill	70 A	20-25	(22.5)	:	48 J	18-24	(21.8)
Tarsus	68 A	39-46	(41.6)	:	49 J	39-44	(41.0)

REFERENCES Moult 76, Biometrics, Weight 68.

GOLDEN PLOVER   *Pluvialis apricaria*

NW P. Short- to medium-distance migrant.

IDENTIFICATION Largish plover; from *P. dominica* by larger size, white underwing and axillaries, proportionately shorter legs and smaller bill, and less bold supercilium. Black underparts in *SP* never include under tail coverts, and flanks also retain some white in full *SP*. Wingbar slightly bolder, with some white on webs of inner primaries. Bill black, legs dull greenish-grey. Larger juvenile *P. squatarola* has black axillaries and bold white wingbar and rump.

AGEING

Ad SP Belly and breast black and, variably depending on race and sex, throat and face also.

WP Feathers of breast, mantle and scapulars with fairly even warm gold edges; on breast and mantle there is no central dark wedge interrupting fringe but there is a narrow one on scapulars. Belly feathers white. Moult from late May on breeding grounds, completing early October; primaries fresh in winter, slightly worn in spring. *SP* often gained late February/March.

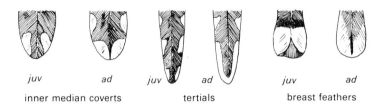

juv	ad	juv	ad	juv	ad
inner median coverts		tertials		breast feathers	

Juv Gold spotting a little paler and duller than *Ad.* Breast, mantle and scapulars with distinct spots; all feathers with dark central terminal wedge which expands distally to form dark band at tip. Belly and flanks white but extensively tipped pale brown.

IW *Juv* characters visible to October but later are difficult; best are tertials and scapulars, usually reliable to November and often midwinter, and dark-tipped belly and flank feathers which may also be retained to midwinter. Primaries only slightly more worn than *Ad* and can be difficult before late winter.

IS Combination of worn greyish coverts with indistinct pale areas, moderately worn primaries, and partial *SP* (usually attained late in April/May).

SEXING Not safely distinguished except in full *SP*, best in nesting pairs. ♂ with clear black breast and belly, without brownish tinge or whitish feathers. ♀ less bright with some brownish and usually many whitish feathers on belly. In *P.a. altifrons* ♂ with clear black bar between bill and white forehead, and black ear-coverts, ♀ with bar between bill and forehead indistinct or absent, and ear-coverts mainly brown/gold. In *P.a. apricaria* ♂ as ♀ *altifrons*, ♀ with white band on neck lacking or very indistinct.

GEOGRAPHICAL VARIATION Two races recognised, *altifrons* ('Northern': Iceland, N. Scandinavia to central USSR) and nominate *apricaria* ('Southern': Ireland to S. Finland). Only differ in *SP*. Typically *altifrons* has clear white supercilium, black face and throat, while *apricaria* has black restricted to breast and belly, and throat dusky. There are however many intermediate patterns indicating a far from complete separation.

67

BIOMETRICS (forms similar)

Wing	54 A♂	177-197	(186.6)	:	13 J♂	176-193	(184.6)
	25 A♀	170-195	(184.6)	:	12 J♀	180-192	(185.8)
Bill	82 A	21-25	(22.5)	:	30 J	21-25	(22.4)
Tarsus	87 A	38-43	(40.3)	:	29 J	38-42	(40.0)

REFERENCES Moult 76, Variation 15, 168.

GREY PLOVER *Pluvialis squatarola*

N N, NC and NE P. Medium- to long-distance migrant.

IDENTIFICATION ·Largish plover, always from *P. dominica* and *P. apricaria* by black axillaries, bold white wingbar and white rump, and larger size. In post-juvenile plumages much greyer than other plovers, except for juvenile *P.d. dominica.* Black extensive on face and flanks in *SP*, but under-tail coverts white. Silvery upperparts distinctive in *SP.* Rather heavy black bill, legs greyish or blackish. *See Plate 3.*

AGEING

Ad SP Upperparts marbled brilliant silver and dark grey. White band above eye and down neck. Underparts black but under-tail coverts and rear belly white.

WP Upperparts and coverts brownish-grey with whitish fringes. Underparts white although some black often retained to early winter. Moult is complex, usually starting August and completing between October and December, but often with a suspension. Some birds do not complete until spring, and so retain old worn outer primaries throughout winter. A few do not complete moult until the subsequent autumn, when two moult cycles may occur together. Thus usually determined in winter by fresh primaries or contrast between fresh inners and worn outers.

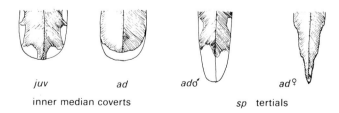

juv   ad   ad♂   ad♀

inner median coverts   *sp* tertials

Juv Upperparts and coverts greyish-brown, with margins boldly spotted pale gold or yellowish-white. Underparts white but very extensive buff-brown barring on breast and flanks.

IW Upperparts and coverts remain distinctly spotted (slightly less clear in south of range). The *Juv* inner medians are retained to spring, but when these coverts wear the pale areas are lost to leave dark central wedges. Underparts white, with darkish fringes lost although central wedge is often retained. Primaries slightly worn in winter, moderately worn in spring.

IS Often with retained *Juv* inner medians; the spots are now a very pale cream. Usually remain in full *WP*. Primaries worn, moulting May-August. (As they complete at least two months before *Ad*, *2W* birds might be identifiable from *Ad WP* by relatively worn primaries).

SEXING Only in *SP*. Underparts black with few whitish fringes (♂), brownish-black/black with many whitish feathers (♀). Also ♀ has largish brown bars on under-tail coverts, ♂ small bars. In Nearctic, ♀ is browner on back and has less contrasting white band and blackish underparts.

SP tertials also useful (see diagram).

GEOGRAPHICAL VARIATION No races recognised but there are clines in winglength. These increase from W to E across Palaearctic and from E to W across Nearctic (see below).

winglength	Canada	Alaska E. Palaearctic	W. Palaearctic
Ad	29; 186-205 (192.7) :	23; 192-213 (201.3) :	72; 186-215 (198.9)
Juv	33; 178-200 (189.1) :	39; 184-206 (196.0) :	54; 183-202 (193.6)

BIOMETRICS *(W. Palaearctic)*

Wing	35 A♂	190-215	(198.2) :	28 J♂	183-202	(194.1)
	53 A♀	186-207	(199.5) :	16 J♀	184-201	(194.6)
Bill	106 A	25-34	(29.0) :	87 J	24-33	(27.9)
Tarsus	107 A	42-52	(46.4) :	88 J	42-50	(46.0)

REFERENCES Moult 6, 9, 76, Variation 16, 21, Biometrics 9, 65, Weight 9, 65, 86, 92, 117.

SPUR-WINGED PLOVER Hoplopterus spinosus

SC P. Resident or short-distance migrant (E).

IDENTIFICATION Smallish lapwing with grey-brown mantle, scapulars and coverts, with white across tips of median and greater coverts and white bases to inner secondaries. Primaries, primary coverts and secondaries black. Upper-tail coverts and base of tail white, outer half of tail black. Underwing coverts, axillaries and under-tail coverts white; rest of underparts black except for large triangular white patches around sides of neck, meeting on nape. Cap black. Bill and legs black. Small curved black spur on carpal joint.

AGEING

Ad   Strikingly black and white. East and North African birds moult primaries May–September (October), so remain fresh to March and are then only slightly worn.

Juv   General colour blackish-brown. Coverts with extensive buff fringes.

IW   Black body plumage attained by October—November, but fringes especially on inner coverts are retained to March—April. Primaries moderately worn in December and very worn in April.

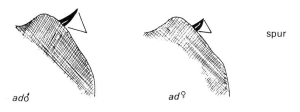

ad♂   *ad♀*   spur

SEXING *Ad* Spur length a useful guide:— ♂ > 11.5mm, ♀ < 7.5mm. This sexes about 50% of birds.

BIOMETRICS

Wing	21 A♂	196-214	(204.1)	:	3 J♂	191-201	(197.3)
	25 A♀	190-209	(200.6)	:	4 J♀	191-201	(194.3)
Bill	63 A	27-33	(29.8)	:	10 J	27-32	(29.1)
Tarsus	63 A	60-78	(68.6)	:	10 J	61-73	(68.6)

BLACKHEAD PLOVER   *Hoplopterus tectus*

Vagrant only to SC P. (E).

IDENTIFICATION   Smallish lapwing with short black crest, and red wattle in front of eye. Head black except for white above and below bill and long white eyestripe. Black throat extends as a narrow black line down centre of breast. Upperparts and sides of breast pale brown. Coverts brown with greaters tipped white; primary coverts and bases to primaries and secondaries white, remiges black distally. Upper tail coverts and base of tail white, distal half of tail black. Bill red with black tip, legs maroon-red.

GREY-HEADED LAPWING   *Vanellus cinereus*

ME P. Short- to medium-distance migrant.

IDENTIFICATION Largish lapwing with black-tipped yellow bill, yellowish legs and small yellow wattle in front of eye. Upperparts brown bordered white across tips of greater coverts. Head and breast brown, more or less suffused ash-grey, with a blackish band across lower breast. Rest of underparts white, underwing coverts white. Upper-tail coverts and tail white, with blackish-brown subterminal tailband across all but outer feathers, broadest on central pair. Primaries black, secondaries white. Very short spur on carpal joint.

AGEING

Ad SP Head and neck plain pale slate-grey. Coverts uniform pale brown. Breast as head, bordered below by blackish band. Belly white.

WP Head and neck brown, tinged grey; chin whitish streaked brown. Mantle brown, coverts brown with very narrow paler tips. Underparts as *SP* but breastband partly obscured. Moult in autumn, so primaries fresh in winter and slightly worn in spring.

Juv Upperparts as *Ad WP* but extensively fringed buff, brightest on inner medians. Underparts as *Ad WP*, but breastband absent or brownish and poorly defined.

IW As *Ad WP* but *Juv* inner medians are retained to late winter, sometimes summer. Primaries slightly worn in winter, moderately worn by spring.

IS Occasionally by retained inner medians. Primaries moderately worn.

SEXING   No characters found.

BIOMETRICS

Wing	13 A♂	235-257	(244.5) :	6 J♂	231-242	(237.2)
	8 A♀	232-247	(242.0) :	4 J♀	231-236	(234.0)
Bill	33 A	34-39	(37.2) :	16 J	34-40	(36.7)
Tarsus	34 A	70-82	(76.9) :	16 J	69-84	(77.3)

RED-WATTLED LAPWING   *Vanellus indicus*

SC and SE P. Mainly resident. (O).

IDENTIFICATION   Lapwing with black-tipped red bill, long yellow legs, and sizeable red wattle in front of eye. Upperparts pale brown with strong green suffusion, and some purplish especially on median coverts. Wing pattern as *H. spinosus* but white bar across covert-tips more clearly defined and one or two inner secondaries wholly white. Upper-tail coverts and tail white with broad black tailband leaving broad white terminal zone (replaced by pale brown on central pair). Cap, face, throat and breast black, with rest of underparts white and variable amount of white on ear-coverts and sides of neck.

AGEING

Ad   (All year) Coverts uniform brown with purplish sheen. During moult black crown is tinged brown and black throat becomes whitish. Moult during autumn, so primaries fresh in winter and slightly worn in spring.

Juv   As *Ad* but black on head and breast is replaced by brown, and chin is white. Coverts brown with buff fringes.

IW   Buff fringes on especially inner medians remain clear in western birds throughout winter but in eastern birds appear to be lost by December. Primaries slightly worn in winter, moderately worn by spring.

IS   Very worn primaries.

SEXING   No characters found.

GEOGRAPHICAL VARIATION   One Palaearctic race recognised, *aigneri* (Iraq-W. Pakistan). Also two adjacent races, nominate *indicus* (India) and *atronuchalis* (Burma eastwards), and one other, *lankae* (Ceylon). In plumage, *aigneri* is similar to *indicus,* but in *atronuchalis* white on the head and neck is reduced to a patch on ear coverts and a white line separating the black nape from the green/brown mantle. There is a cline of decreasing winglength from W to E:-*aigneri* (232.5), *indicus* (north: 229.0), *atronuchalis* (217.3) and *lankae* (217.6).

BIOMETRICS   *V.i. aigneri*

Wing	8 A♂	228-245	(234.0)	: 6 J	210-229	(220.7)
	7 A♀	216-240	(230.6)	:		
Bill	20 A	31-36	(33.9)	: 5 J	31-35	(33.4)
Tarsus	20 A	70-83	(77.4)	: 6 J	74-78	(76.3)

SOCIABLE PLOVER   *Chettusia gregaria*

MC P. Medium-distance migrant.

IDENTIFICATION   Smallish lapwing, mainly grey-brown with white or whitish supercilia; bill black, legs blackish. Primaries black, secondaries white, coverts grey-brown with greaters tipped white. Upper-tail coverts and tail white, with blackish subterminal tailband not extending to outer two pairs. Chestnut and black belly, black crown, and yellowish throat and cheeks very distinctive in *SP,* belly whitish and head more uniform in winter and juvenile.

AGEING

Ad SP Black crown, broad white supercilia. Throat and ear-coverts yellowish. Coverts uniform darkish grey-brown, at first with pale sandy fringes. Belly black with chestnut around vent.

WP Crown mostly brown, supercilia brownish-buff. Breast whitish mottled brown, belly white. Coverts as *SP*, rapidly wearing to uniform colour. Moult during summer, completing September, so primaries are fresh in midwinter and slightly worn in spring.

Juv Similar to *Ad WP* but upperparts have very extensive buff fringes and subterminal darker areas. Coverts dark grey-brown with pale buff fringes; feathers appearing much smaller than the sandy-fringed coverts of fresh *Ad*. Breast with distinct dark V-shaped flecks.

IW As *Ad WP* but buff-fringed inner medians retained to spring. Primaries slightly worn in winter, moderately worn in spring.

IS Some retain a few *Juv* inner medians, but best told by very worn primaries. Usually attain partial *SP* but breast with brown mottling and belly mostly white.

SEXING Only possible for *Ad SP* but considerable variation: ♀ tends to have brownish-black belly with some whitish feathers, and less chestnut around vent than ♂. ♂ averages slightly larger.

BIOMETRICS

Wing	21 A♂	201-215	(207.7) : 11 J♂	198-212	(205.0)
	16 A♀	195-221	(203.5) : 12 J♀	197-209	(203.1)
Bill	55 A	25-33	(29.8) : 34 J	26-31	(29.2)
Tarsus	59 A	55-64	(60.1) : 33 J	54-63	(58.9)

WHITE-TAILED PLOVER   *Chettusia leucura*

SC P. Resident or short-distance migrant.

IDENTIFICATION Smallish lapwing with black bill and long yellow legs. Upperparts grey-brown with strong lilac sheen. Head mainly brown with paler face; breast strongly grey; centre of belly rosy-buff. Median and greater coverts grey, with black subterminal bands and broad white tips to greaters and outer medians. Primaries black, secondaries white, but outer secondaries tipped black and some white on inner primaries. Upper-tail coverts and tail completely white, or with fine brown terminal markings in juvenile.

AGEING

Ad (All year). Mantle and coverts even grey-brown, tinged lilac. Breast grey. Moult in autumn, completing by December, so in winter and spring primaries are fresh.

Juv Mantle boldly patterned with black and yellow-buff blotches. Coverts greyish, strikingly edged buff. Breast and neck brownish-grey with paler edges. Tail feathers with small brownish subterminal band and narrow buffish tips.

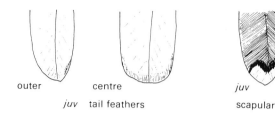

outer   centre   *juv*

juv   tail feathers   scapular

IW   Back pattern lost by October; inner medians retain buff tips but fade and abrade by March. Outer webs of outer tail feathers retain brownish marks until January. Primaries slightly worn in winter, moderately worn by spring.

IS   Only by moderately worn primaries.

SEXING   No known plumage characters.

BIOMETRICS

Wing	19 A♂	174-185	(180.3) : 10 J♂	172-186	(179.9)
	24 A♀	170-185	(177.3) : 11 J♀	175-187	(180.5)
Bill	62 A	27-32	(29.6) : 38 J	26-32	(29.5)
Tarsus	62 A	65-78	(71.4) : 38 J	63-77	(70.5)

LAPWING   *Vanellus vanellus*

M P. Resident or short- to medium-distance migrant.

IDENTIFICATION   Large plover with long wispy crest and wings exceptionally broad and rounded. Crown and crest black, face black and white. Underparts white except for broad black breastband and orange-brown under tail coverts, but throat and upper breast also black in breeding males. Upperparts strongly glossy green, fringed reddish-buff when fresh. Scapulars have some glossy purple, and sheen on lessers and medians may be blue or bluish. Longest upper tail coverts orange-brown. Remiges black with brownish-white markings towards tips of outer primaries. Tail white with broad black distally (less black on outer feathers). Bill blackish, legs dull reddish-flesh.

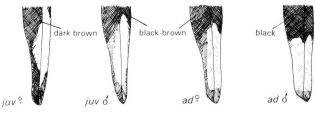

juv ♀   *juv* ♂   *ad* ♀   *ad* ♂

tip of 10th primary

74

AGEING The principal characters for ageing and sexing are tabulated below. Others of help are:

Ad Coverts uniform green/blue; many of these, also mantle and scapulars, have broad red-buff tips in autumn but these are lost during the winter. They are of a different form to the narrow fringes of *Juv* inner lessers and medians. Moult May-October, so primaries are fresh in winter and slightly worn in spring.

Juv Coverts with narrow buff fringes (not tips); feathers appear small. Breastband brownish.

IW Coverts either lose fringes or are replaced by winter. Primaries slightly worn in midwinter, more worn in spring, but difference from *Ad* wear pattern is relatively small.

IS Very difficult unless primaries are moderately worn.

ad♂   juv♀

Summary of ageing/sexing criteria of Lapwing

	Ad♂		*A♀*
wing formula	10=4/5 (3-5)	:	10=6/7 (7)
10th (outer) primary	—see diagram		
crest length	most 80 +	:	most 60-75
lesser coverts	blue	:	greenish-blue
outer tail feathers	black/white	:	black/white
	IW♂		*IW♀*
wing formula	10=6/7 (7)	:	10=8/9 (7-9)
10th (outer) primary	—see diagram		
crest length	most 70 +	:	most 40-60
lesser coverts	bluish-green	:	green
outer tail feathers	white, little black	:	white, little black

Of these the lesser coverts can be difficult to use and the outer tail-feather pattern is variable. Typically *Juv/IW* have the outer tail feather all white, but all ages may have black on the inner web although in *Ad* it tends to spread to the outer web too.

75

SEXING See table above. Also *Ad SP ♂* usually has completely black upper breast, throat and face pattern, while ♀ usually has whitish feathers in this black area. Crest length is helpful, see below.

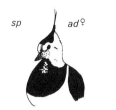 

sp   ad♀   ad♂

Crest length (not usable for *Ad* in moult).

	Ad♂		*A♀*
March-June	14, 74-104 (88.1)	:	8, 68-76 (73.0)
November-February	9, 72-100 (88.3)	:	11, 50-80 (63.5)
	IW♂		*IW♀*
July-October	6, 54-57 (55.2)	:	7, 26-54 (40.3)
November-March	14, 52-91 (79.2)	:	4, 43-75 (54.7)

BIOMETRICS

Wing	29 A♂	214-237	(228.7) : 21 J♂	215-233	(222.2)
	22 A♀	218-234	(225.5) : 16 J♀	210-229	(220.6)
Bill	54 A	22-28	(25.0) : 36 J	23-28	(24.9)
Tarsus	57 A	43-50	(46.5) : 38 J	44-49	(46.6)

REFERENCES Age 31, 75, Moult 42, Sex 12, 31, 75, Biometrics 12, 71, 75, Weight 42, 71.

SURFBIRD   *Aphriza virgata*

NW N (SE Alaska only). Short-, medium- or long-distance migrant.

IDENTIFICATION Calidrid-like in general aspect and recalling *C. maritima* and *C. ptilocnemis* in *WP*, but much larger than these and with shortish plover-like bill. Upperparts, head and breast mainly slate-grey, dappled with white and chestnut in *SP*, underparts otherwise white with blackish spots and Vs on flanks. Long narrow white wingbar. Tail white at base but black distally, and uppertail coverts also clear white making a striking pattern. Bill dusky with yellow base to lower mandible, legs short and yellow. See also *Arenaria melanocephala*.

AGEING

Ad SP Mantle and scapulars slate-grey with some bold chestnut and white feathers. Coverts uniform grey with whitish edges. Underparts white but breast spotted blackish and flanks with many blackish V marks.

WP Mantle and coverts slate-grey. Breast slate-grey with indistinct brownish spots, belly white with brownish Vs and spots on flanks. Clear white fringes on tips of primaries 1-5. Moult starts in late autumn, appears to suspend and complete during late winter; primaries are fresh in winter/spring, and slightly worn in autumn.

Juv Coverts greyish-brown with pale buff fringes and clear dark subterminal bar. Breast brownish.

IW As *Ad WP*, but with retained *Juv* coverts. Fringes wear off, but dark subterminal bar is usually present on inner medians to spring. Whitish tips on some inner primaries but these less extensive than in *Ad*. Primaries are slightly worn in winter, moderately worn in spring.

IS Very worn primaries; may attain a partial *SP*.

SEXING   No plumage characters found.

BIOMETRICS   Only very small samples measured — sexes combined.

Wing	8 A		174-183	(176.7)	:	11 J	169-185	(179.4)
Bill	8 A		22-26	(24.0)	:	11 J	22-27	(24.4)
Tarsus	8 A		29-31	(30.0)	:	11 J	29-32	(30.6)

GREATER KNOT   *Calidris tenuirostris*

NE P. Medium- to long-distance migrant.

IDENTIFICATION   Largest calidrid, with structure and tail-pattern recalling *C. canutus,* but larger than this species, with a proportionately longer and thinner bill, and lacking the clear wingbar and red on underparts in *SP*. Ground colour to upper tail coverts whitish, but heavily obscured by spotting and barring of grey or blackish. Tail feathers uniformly darkish grey-brown. White tips to greater coverts but not forming a contrasting wingbar. Bill blackish, brownish at base; legs dull greenish-grey.

AGEING

Ad SP Back brownish-black, at first obscured by buffish or greyish-white tips. Scapulars, sometimes tertials, with large chestnut spots. Coverts grey-brown with white fringes. Throat finely spotted and neck streaked with blackish-brown; breast heavily spotted forming almost a blackish-brown band, the bold spots extending down flanks and sometimes onto belly. Rest of underparts white.

WP   Mantle and coverts grey; outer coverts edged paler grey, inners edged white. Underparts white, with breast finely streaked and spotted pale brown. Moult September-December, so primaries are fresh in winter and slightly worn in spring.

Juv   Upperparts blackish-brown with pale buff tips. Coverts grey-brown broadly fringed whitish-buff with small subterminal dark smudge on inners. Underparts white; breast with pale brown spots and streaks, and a few streaks on flanks. Inner primaries with sharply defined white tips.

IW   As *Ad WP* but some brownish coverts with pale buff tips, especially inner medians, are retained to spring. Tertials are patterned as coverts but these also are lost by early spring. White-tipped *Juv* primaries wear rapidly, so are moderately worn by spring.

IS   Only by moderately worn primaries, although some may renew outers. Many attain *SP*.

SEXING   ♀ may have less red on upperparts in *SP*. ♀ averages larger.

BIOMETRICS

Wing	14 A♂	179-193	(185.7) :	16 J♂	170-184	(176.3)
	21 A♀	181-198	(190.7) :	11 J♀	171-189	(180.4)
Bill	13 A♂	39-45	(42.4) :	12 J♂	40-45	(42.3)
	18 A♀	41-47	(43.9) :	11 J♀	39-43	(41.5)
Tarsus	47 A	32-38	(34.7) :	39 J	32-36	(34.4)

REFERENCES   Biometrics, Weight 155.

KNOT   *Calidris canutus*

N H (fragmented). Medium- to long-distance migrant.

IDENTIFICATION   Large calidrid with rump whitish barred grey as in *C. tenuirostris*, but much smaller and with a bolder wingbar. Shares pale rump and chestnut-red underparts in *SP* with *C. ferruginea*, but has duller rump, shorter paler legs, and a shorter straighter bill than this species. Much larger and heavier than *C. fuscicollis*. Bill blackish, legs dull greenish. *See Plate 4.*

AGEING

Ad SP   Upperparts with dark brown centres and yellowish/rufous edges. Coverts grey, fringed white. Underparts chestnut.

WP   Upperparts and coverts grey, latter with some narrow white fringes. Underparts whitish with grey suffusion and streaking on breast. Moult timing varies with latitude: in Europe and N. Africa July-November, so primaries are fresh in winter and slightly worn in spring; in S. Africa October-February, so are fresh in spring, worn in autumn. In Nearctic appear to moult inners in the north August-October, suspend and complete outers in S. America January-March, so are fresh in spring.

coverts , tertials

ad   juv

Juv   Upperparts and coverts greyish-brown with characteristic pale fringe and dark subterminal line. Underparts whitish strongly washed pink-buff.

IW   As *Ad WP* but some inner grey-brown coverts with subterminal bars remain, and even when these bars have been lost the brownish coverts are distinctive. In Europe primaries are slightly worn in winter, moderately worn in spring. In S. Africa there is a variable primary moult (inners, outers, or complete) between January and July, so either with moderately worn primaries or showing active moult in late winter/spring.

IS   Usually a few *Juv* coverts remain. Others only by primary wear pattern and moult — in Europe moderately worn with moult May-August, in S. Africa a complete moult July-December. Usually remain in *WP*.

2W   Particularly in S. hemisphere the moult pattern may enable identification, *2W* being relatively less worn than *Ad* after completion of moult. Also some *'Ads'* with subterminal bars to coverts may be *2W*.

SEXING *SP* Underparts: ♂ with even chestnut, ♀ with many whitish feathers admixed (but see racial variation). Mantle: ♂ with chestnut, ♀ much greyer.

size   ♀ averages larger.

GEOGRAPHICAL VARIATION Three races recognised: nominate *canutus* (NE Canada, Greenland, central USSR), *rogersi* (NE USSR) and *rufa* (central Canada). Separated in *SP* by:—

	bill length average	underpart colour	rear belly (white patch)	mantle fringes
C.c. canutus:				
Can./Greenland	♂32 ♀34	deep chestnut	very small	many yellowish
Siberia	♂35 ♀36	deep chestnut	very small	rich rufous
C.c. rogersi	♂32 ♀34	chestnut	fairly large	rufous
C.c. rufa	♂35 ♀36	pale chestnut	large	rufous

BIOMETRICS   *C.c. canutus* : (Canada/Greenland)

Wing	29 A♂	160-176	(167.9) :	36 J♂	156-167	(160.9)
	17 A♀	167-177	(170.5) :	26 J♀	157-168	(162.6)
Bill	28 A♂	29-36	(32.6) :	36 J♂	28-36	(31.7)
	18 A♀	31-37	(34.2) :	26 J♀	30-37	(33.3)
Tarsus	34 A	29-33	(31.7) :	31 J	27-33	(30.7)

Wing and tarsus are similar for all populations and bill length for *rogersi* is similar to above, the bill length for the other two groups differs:—

C.c. canutus (Siberia) ♂ 34.5 SE ±0.2 (n=26), ♀35.9 SE ±0.3 (n=17).

C.c. rufa   9 A♂ 33-38 (34.7) : 18 J 30-39 (32.2)
          8 A♀ 35-38 (36.5) :

REFERENCES   Moult 6, 164, Sex 23, 59, Variation 18, 23, 37, Biometrics 23, 37, 44B, 94, 95, 97, 121, Weights 44B, 92, 94, 95, 97, 127, 128.

SANDERLING   *Calidris alba*

N H '(fragmented). Medium- to long-distance migrant.

IDENTIFICATION   Medium-sized calidrid with black bill and legs, very clear white wingbar and white sides to rump. Only calidrid lacking hind toe. In *WP* whitish-grey upperparts contrasting with blackish leading edge to wing are distinctive; in *SP* recalls stints but is considerably larger. In juvenile, predominantly whitish spotting on blackish upperparts is characteristic. *See Plate 3.*

AGEING

Ad SP Head and breast extensively spotted rufous and blackish with a distinct division against white underparts. Back blackish with rufous and grey edges, at first obscured by white/grey tips. Coverts grey, outers edged paler and inners fringed white.

WP   Back and crown grey; coverts grey with white fringes; underparts white. Moult August-October in the north, so primaries are fresh in winter and slightly worn in spring/summer. In S. Africa moult is mid October-end February so primaries are fresh in winter/spring.

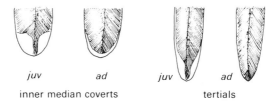

juv   ad   juv   ad
inner median coverts   tertials

Juv   Cap and back blackish, extensively spotted whitish-buff. Tertials and coverts blackish-brown with wide fringe formed by large buff spots; inner medians, tertials and rump feathers with thin terminal dark fringe. Underparts white, with breast washed buff at first.

IW   As *Ad WP* but with worn brownish tertials and coverts with remnants of spots. Inner medians and 5th tertial may have trace of terminal fringe until spring and sometimes summer, depending on wintering area and moult. In the north primaries are slightly worn in midwinter, moderately worn in spring. In southern hemisphere there is a variable moult, complete or outer primaries only, starting anytime from January to July.

IS   Occasionally worn *Juv* inner medians are retained, but usually by moderate wear/moult pattern of primaries. Very few attain *SP* and reach breeding grounds. In the south often in moult from late winter.

2W   Southern birds start moult immediately after *IW/IS* moult and sometimes have two moults in progress at same time.

SEXING   In *SP* back of ♂ black/red-brown, of ♀ black/greyish, and ♀ tends to have more unmoulted coverts (safe to use only on pairs). ♀ averages slightly larger.

GEOGRAPHICAL VARIATION   No races recognised but Canadian birds tend to be richest red on back in *SP* (sex difference is apparent everywhere). Measurements similar in all, although possibly Siberian bill lengths average 1mm longer than the others (♂ 25.0, ♀ 26.2).

BIOMETRICS

Wing	30 A♂	120-131	(125.1) :	49 J♂	116-129	(123.2)
	34 A♀	119-131	(127.2) :	65 J♀	119-133	(125.7)
Bill	18 A♂	21-26	(24.0) :	40 J♂	21-27	(24.1)
	19 A♀	22-27	(25.2) :	52 J♀	21-28	(25.1)
Tarsus	17 A♂	22-27	(24.2) :	41 J♂	22-26	(24.0)
	19 A♀	24-27	(24.9) :	51 J♀	23-27	(24.5)

REFERENCES   Moult 6, 164, Biometrics 44B, 117, 143A, Weight 44B 92, 117.

TABLE 2 Identification of the Seven Small Calidrids

	Distinctive Features	Leg Colour & Base to Bill	Bill Shape	Juv Plumage
C. pusilla	palmations	black or greenish-black	rather deep at base and with laterally expanded tip	often rather dull earth-brown above, with blackish-brown on cap, back and scapulars edged chestnut and pale buff
C. mauri	palmations	black or greenish-black	similar to C. pusilla but averaging longer and usually with slightly drooped bill-tip	very similar to C. pusilla but slightly brighter, including some rufous-chestnut and whitish-buff fringes
C. ruficollis		black	very similar to C. pusilla but with base less deep and tip less expanded	very similar to C. pusilla and C. mauri, but not as dull as some C. pusilla. Lacks clear V-markings of C. minuta, and central tail feathers differ in shape and pattern (see text).
C. minuta		black	very similar to C. ruficollis but with base less deep and tip less expanded	rather brighter than other dark-legged species and with paler nape. Whitish-buff fringes on back forming a clear V-mark
C. temminckii	white/whitish outer tail feathers	greenish brownish or yellowish	shallow at base and tip very fine, sometimes slightly decurved	Strikingly different. Plain brownish-grey above, feathers with dark shaft-streaks and subterminal bands, and narrow buff fringes. Breast clear grey
C. subminuta	long toes	greenish or yellowish	as C. temminckii but slightly deeper at base, and tip less fine	brightly-patterned, similar to C. minuta but lacking pale nape. Rich chestnut fringes predominating, but whitish-buff on back forming a V-mark
C. minutilla		greenish or yellowish	as C. subminuta	very similar to C. subminuta

Summer Plumage	Distinctive measurements
some rufous admixed on cap, ear-coverts and mantle. Fine brown streaks forming band across upper breast.	bill range at least 15.1-23.9 mm. In difficult cases, measure: distal corner of nostril to tip of bill and bill width at narrow point just behind nail. (Sexing is important if possible).
much brighter than *C. pusilla* in full plumage. Rufous ear-coverts and much rufous admixed on cap and mantle. Strongly streaked and spotted breast with spots extending down flanks to under tail coverts.	bill range at least 20.2-28.8 mm. Some will not be separable unless sexed, but see *C. pusilla* for additional helpful measurements. Beware geographical variation in *C. pusilla*.
cap, nape and mantle feathers with broad rufous-chestnut sides, and tipped pale grey-brown when fresh. Throat, cheeks and upper breast clear chestnut-red, with some brown spotting at sides of breast.	wing/tarsus of live birds tells most from *C. minuta*, but 2-5% are in the overlap zone. Wing/tarsus of $\geqslant 5.1$ indicates this species.
cap, nape and mantle with broad orange-chestnut sides and fringes. Throat white; brown spotting on orange-chestnut suffusion forming band on upper breast.	wing/tarsus of $\leqslant 5.0$ is this species rather than *C. ruficollis*, but beware small overlap zone between 5.0 and 5.1.
much duller and more uniform. Dark grey-brown cap, nape and mantle, fringed and mottled with dull chestnut and buff. Throat and breast suffused grey-brown and brown with darker streaking.	tail-feathers 5 and 6 about equal in length, as in *C. subminuta* and *C. minutilla*, (but 6 is 2+ mm. longer in other species in this table).
similar to *C. pusilla* but darker above and lacking distinct rufous on ear-coverts and cap. Streaking on breast more diffuse, extending onto flanks, but not as distinctively marked as *C. mauri*.	central toe (to base of claw) is 20-23 mm; with claw approx. 22-26 mm.
very similar to *C. subminuta*—dark above with rather narrow **edges and fringes**. Streaking on breast often forming a clear band, extending slightly onto flanks.	central toe (to base of claw) is 16-19 mm; with claw approx. 18-21 mm.

SEMIPALMATED SANDPIPER   *Calidris pusilla*

N N. Medium- to long-distance migrant.

IDENTIFICATION   Small calidrid, often difficult to separate from similar species (but see Table 2). In the hand, from all but *C. mauri* by partial webbing between bases of all front toes. Often from *C. mauri* on bill-length, but note geographical variation in present species. Shares narrow white wingbar and white sides to rump with other small calidrids.

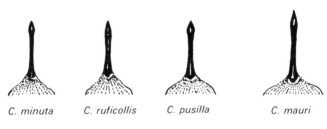

C. minuta   C. ruficollis   C. pusilla   C. mauri

bills from above

AGEING

Ad SP   Resembles dull *C. mauri* but ear-coverts and nape patch are very dull chestnut, scapulars lack bright chestnut bases, and breast is slightly less heavily spotted and streaked brown. Coverts grey-brown; outers are paler at tip, inners are whitish-fringed.

WP   As *C. mauri*. Coverts as *SP*. Moult is October-February, so primaries are fresh in spring.

Juv   Often as *C. mauri*, both having considerable range of pale or rich buff/chestnut/whitish fringes on mantle and scapulars. The coverts have buff fringes.

IW   As *Ad WP* but some inner medians with buff fringes are retained to spring. Some do not moult, so have slightly worn primaries in winter and moderately worn in spring; others moult outer primaries, so have contrast between worn inners and new outers in spring/summer.

IS   Most attain *SP* and lose inner medians during prenuptial moult; these can only be identified on moderately worn primaries, or contrast of old inners and fresh outers.

SEXING   Only bill length is a guide (but see geographical variation), as ♀ averages slightly larger.

GEOGRAPHICAL VARIATION   No races but bill length decreases from Alaska to E. Canada, ♂ $\bar{x}$ 19.5-17.4, ♀   21.4-19.1.

Wing	22 A♂	93-103	(97.4)	:	13 J♂	93-99	(96.3)
	16 A♀	94-104	(98.6)	:	16 J♀	93-100	(97.6)
Bill	14 A♂	16-21	(18.6)	:	9 J♂	15-19	(17.8)
	11 A♀	18-22	(20.2)	:	9 J♀	18-21	(19.7)
Tarsus	14 A♂	19-22	(20.6)	:	9 J♂	20-22	(20.9)
	11 A♀	20-23	(21.4)	:	9 J♀	20-22	(21.7)

REFERENCES   Ident. 115, 161, Age 14, Biometrics 104, Weight 86, 97B, 110.

WESTERN SANDPIPER   *Calidris mauri*

NW N (also extreme NE P). Medium- to long-distance migrant.

IDENTIFICATION   Small calidrid, see *C. pusilla* and Table 2. Bill usually longer than in other small species and with a distinct downturn at tip, but beware upper end of *C. pusilla* range. Some unsexed birds in winter and juvenile plumage may not be separable in the hand from *C. pusilla* using present knowledge, but see Table 2 for additional useful measurements.

AGEING
Ad SP   Upperparts blackish-brown, with conspicuous broad chestnut edging especially to rear crown, ear-coverts and scapulars. Scapulars have chestnut bases. Coverts grey-brown; outers are paler at tip, and inners are fringed whitish. Underparts whitish, with breast heavily spotted and streaked brown, and some brown flank spots.

WP   Upperparts uniform grey-brown; whitish forehead and small white supercilium. Coverts as *SP*. Underparts white, with finely streaked breastband suffused grey-brown at sides. Moult July-October in the north, so primaries are fresh in winter and slightly worn by spring, but October-February in the south, so these are fresh in spring.

Juv   Upperparts brownish-black with fairly prominent bright chestnut and whitish edges. Coverts grey-brown, outers edged bright buff, inners chestnut-brown. Underparts white with breast washed pale buffish and finely streaked.

IW   As *Ad WP* but buff-tipped inner medians retained. Primaries slightly worn in winter, moderately worn by spring.

IS   Inner medians lost, so can only be identified on very worn primaries. Most attain *SP* but some of those summering in the south start primary moult in May-June.

SEXING   Although ranges overlap, bill length can be a useful guide to assess the proportions of each sex in a sample; the division is ≤ 24 ♂, ≥ 25 ♀ and birds near the division should be measured carefully to 0.5mm.

BIOMETRICS

Wing	13 A♂	94-101	(97.1)	:	6 J♂	94-97	(96.2)
	10 A♀	97-103	(99.9)	:	16 J♀	95-101	(98.1)
Bill	11 A♂	21-29	(23.7)	:	6 J♂	21-24	(22.5)
	10 A♀	21-29	(25.4)	:	15 J♀	23-30	(26.1)
Tarsus	13 A♂	20-23	(21.5)	:	6 J♂	21-22	(21.3)
	10 A♀	20-24	(22.7)	:	16 J♀	21-24	(22.7)

REFERENCES Ident. 104, 161, Moult 64, Sex 108, Biometrics 104, 108, Weight 64, 86, 97B.

RED-NECKED STINT   *Calidris ruficollis*

NE P (also extreme NW N). Medium- to long-distance migrant.

IDENTIFICATION   Small calidrid (see Table 2). Most similar to *C. pusilla*, but lacking palmations, and *C. minuta* but with a usually larger wing/tarsus ratio. Distinctive in *SP*, but note *Eurynorhynchus pygmeus* which is very similar except for spatulate bill. Tail-feathers except central pair rather whiter on inner web than *C. minuta* and *C. pusilla* and sometimes with more distinct white fringe. In *Juv* plumage, central tail feathers more rounded than in *Juv C. minuta* and with a narrower fringe.

C. ruficollis   C. minuta

juv central tail feathers

AGEING

Ad SP   Throat, front of neck and upper breast rich chestnut-red (partly obscured by white tips at first); rest of underparts white but with some brown spots on breast and upper flanks. Cap and back dark brown with rich chestnut edgings. Nape pale brown with chestnut fringes. Coverts grey-brown, with tip paler on outers and inners fringed white.

WP   Forehead white; white supercilium but not extending far past eye. Rest of upperparts uniform pale grey-brown with darker shaft streaks. Coverts grey-brown, inners greyer and with whitish fringes. Underparts white with grey lateral breast patches and almost no streaking. Considerable variation in moult pattern. Northern winterers moult August-December, so primaries are fresh in winter and slightly worn in spring; southern winterers either moult inner primaries in autumn, suspend and complete in wintering area November-March, or moult in winter quarters September-March (both having fresh primaries in spring).

Juv Cap brown with pale chestnut edges, neck greyish streaked brown, back brown edged chestnut; scapulars blackish-brown tipped white and chestnut. Coverts grey-brown, outers fringed cream and inners pale chestnut (much paler than *Juv C. minuta* coverts). Underparts white, with sides of neck and breast (sometimes all of breast) washed buffish-grey with a few fine brown streaks.

IW By mid-October forehead and underparts are very white. Upperparts generally pale grey with some dark shaft streaks. Coverts grey-brown; outers fade and wear, but inners with very pale buff fringes through winter. Primaries are slightly worn in winter and moderately worn by spring; some start to replace outer primaries during April-June.

IS Very difficult to see *Juv* inner medians; may attain a partial *SP*. Best told by primary wear: unmoulted birds are very worn by July/August when start moult from primary 1, the others show contrast of worn inners and fresh outers.

SEXING *SP* of ♀ reported to be paler. ♀ has longer wing than ♂ on average.

BIOMETRICS

Wing	21 A♂	96-108	(102.5) : 21 J♂	95-107	(100.4)
	25 A♀	96-111	(105.2) : 31 J♀	99-108	(102.7)
Bill	14 A	16-19	(17.5) : 34 J	16-20	(17.3)
Tarsus	11 A	19-20	(19.2) : 36 J	18-21	(19.1)

REFERENCES Ident. 161, Moult 29, 147, Weight 145, 147.

LITTLE STINT   *Calidris minuta*

NC P. Long-distance migrant.

IDENTIFICATION Small calidrid (see Table 2). Rather finer bill than other dark-legged small calidrids, and lacking palmations. Most similar to *C. ruficollis*, but most can be identified in the hand on the smaller wing/tarsus ratio. *Juv* central tail feathers are more pointed than in *C. ruficollis* and with central dark wedge reaching a point at tip of feather.

AGEING

Ad SP Cap and nape blackish-brown with rufous/whitish edges. Mantle and scapulars blackish-brown edged and tipped bright rufous, after grey-brown extreme tips have worn off; tertials with greyish tips. Coverts brown with paler edges, inner medians pale grey-brown tipped whitish. Rump with chestnut tips. Ear coverts reddish-brown, throat mostly white, indistinct reddish and brown-speckled gorget on upper breast; rest of underparts white.

WP Upperparts grey-brown with darker shaft streaks. Coverts uniform pale grey-brown, with outers fringed paler but whitish fringes on inners. Underparts white with greyish smudges at side of breast sometimes forming a gorget. Moult timing variable: in India and probably N. Africa complete by October/November; in S. and E. Africa start end September/early October and complete November/March, but they may suspend moult at any time in between. Early completing birds are slightly worn in spring, later birds are fresh.

Juv Cap dark brown edged chestnut; mantle and scapulars brownish-black with bright chestnut and whitish fringes and edges, forming distinct V lines on back. Nape usually noticeably pale grey-brown with brownish streaks. Coverts brown, fringed chestnut on outers and bright chestnut on inners. Underparts whitish but fairly distinct buff band on upper breast, emphasised at sides by indistinct dark mottling. Rump lacks chestnut tips.

IW As *Ad WP* but inner medians with bright chestnut tips retained to February in E. and S. Africa (possibly throughout winter in N.). General colour of coverts brownish. Moult is variable: in E. Africa a minority (<20%) moult outer primaries in early spring, while most have a complete primary moult December/February to March/April. (Possibly N. African/Mediterranean birds do not moult or moult outers only). *Juv* inner medians are replaced during this moult. In spring primaries fresh or, (only in north?), with old inners and new outers.

IS Not reliably separated from late moulting *Ad* unless primaries are all very worn, or there is contrast between old inners and new outers. Attain *SP* but this is rather dull, especially on ear coverts and breast.

SEXING   No plumage characters found. Generally those with bill ⩽ 17 and wing ⩽ 95 are ♂, bill ⩾ 19 and wing ⩾ 99 are ♀.

BIOMETRICS

Wing	15 A♂	92-99	(95.9) : 39 J♂	91-101	(96.6)
	13 A♀	96-103	(99.5) : 43 J♀	92-103	(99.2)
Bill	9 A♂	17-19	(17.8) : 31 J♂	16-19	(17.2)
	13 A♀	17-20	(19.0) : 37 J♀	17-20	(18.5)
Tarsus	9 A♂	19-22	(20.5) : 31 J♂	20-23	(21.0)
	13 A♀	21-22	(21.3) : 37 J♀	20-22	(21.5)

REFERENCES   Ident. 161, Age 152, Moult 91, 112, 120, 153, 164, Sexing 152, Biometrics 27, 117, Weight 91, 113, 117.

TEMMINCK'S STINT   *Calidris temminckii*

N P. Medium- to long-distance migrant.

IDENTIFICATION Easiest small calidrid to identify, as has outer tail feathers 4-6 white or greyish-white and about equal in length. Plumages rather plain, recalling diminutive *Actitis hypoleucos* or *A. macularia*. See Table 2 for comparisons with similar species. Legs are usually greenish, brownish or yellowish, but black has been recorded.

AGEING
Ad SP Cap, mantle and scapulars grey-brown, some with dull brown centres, others edged and tipped dull rufous. All tipped grey when fresh. Coverts brown, tipped brownish-buff on outers, and whitish on inners (they may appear similar to the worn *IS* feathers but are much fresher and buffer). Underparts white, with upper breast greyish-brown, streaked brown.

WP Upperparts very uniform dark grey-brown; coverts as above, inners fringed white. Underparts white, breast strongly washed dark grey-brown (may form lateral patches or complete band). Moult usually starts late July-September, suspends and completes February-April; a few complete by October/November. Therefore either fresh or with new inners and old outers in winter, slightly worn or fresh in spring.

inner median coverts

juv   ad

Juv Upperparts much duller than related species, dark grey-brown with buff fringes and dark subterminal bands. Coverts as upperparts; outers are tipped buff and inners chestnut-buff. Small pale throat, and breast with brown wash; rest of underparts white.

IW As *Ad WP* but inner medians usually retained to summer when are dark brown with worn pale buff/white fringes. Outer primaries moulted December-May, so in late winter/spring show contrast of very worn inners and fresh outers.

IS Often with *Juv* inner medians; inner primaries old, outers fresh. Attain *SP*.

SEXING No characters found, but breeding season weights differ: ♂ 22-26g. (24.3), ♀ 26-29.5 (27.8).

BIOMETRICS
Wing	31 A ♂	94-103	(97.6) : 21 J ♂	96-104	(98.7)
	14 A♀	95-102	(98.1) : 23 J♀	95-104	(99.3)
Bill	30 A	16-18	(16.9) : 21 J	15-19	(16.8)
Tarsus	34 A	17-18	(17.5) : 16 J	17-18	(17.6)

REFERENCES Ident. 161, Sex 57, Biometrics, Weight 57, 155.

89

LONG-TOED STINT   *Calidris subminuta*

NE P. Medium- to long-distance migrant.

IDENTIFICATION   Small calidrid (see Table 2). From *C. temminckii* by stronger patterning of plumage and grey-brown outer tail feathers, from other similar species except *C. minutilla* by greenish or yellowish legs. Larger and less compact than *C. minutilla*, with rather long toes (which may be useful as a field character), and with breastband less well-defined.

AGEING

Ad SP   Upperparts brownish-black with extensive bright chestnut and some greyish-white fringes. Coverts brown, edged pale chestnut; inner medians fringed white. Underparts whitish, with upper breast finely streaked brown-buff.

WP   Upperparts blackish-brown with dark grey-brown fringes. Coverts dark grey-brown, edged paler on outers and fringed whitish on inners. Underparts white but breast with dark greyish-brown smudges and some fine streaks. Moult August-November; primaries are fresh in midwinter, slightly worn by summer.

Juv   Cap and mantle blackish with bright chestnut lateral spots and fringes. Scapulars with some whitish edges. Coverts brown, outers broadly tipped and spotted whitish/buff, inners and tertials with bright chestnut fringes. Underparts whitish, breast smudged grey-brown with some streaks.

IW   As *Ad WP* but *Juv* inner medians retain chestnut tips to spring. Primaries slightly worn in early winter, moderately worn by spring.

IS   Many retain *Juv* inner medians, but these now have pale buff fringes. Primaries worn. Many attain *SP*.

SEXING   ♀ averages slightly larger.

BIOMETRICS

Wing	22 A♂	90-97	(93.5) : 23 J♂	90-97	(92.6)
	30 A♀	91-100	(95.4) : 22 J♀	89-96	(93.4)
Bill	10 A♂	17-19	(17.6) : 6 J♂	17-19	(17.3)
	14 A♀	17-19	(18.3) : 6 J♀	18-20	(18.7)
Tarsus	26 A	20-23	(21.4) : 24 J	21-23	(21.7)

REFERENCES   Ident. 161, Biometrics, Weight 155.

LEAST SANDPIPER   *Calidris minutilla*

N N. Medium- to long-distance migrant.

IDENTIFICATION   Smallest calidrid (see Table 2). Very similar to *C. subminuta* but smaller, more compact, and with a clearer breastband. Central toe measurement is diagnostic in the hand.

AGEING

Ad SP   Crown and mantle blackish with chestnut and buffish-grey fringes. Coverts brown, inners broadly edged greyish-white. Underparts white with upper breast streaked brown.

WP   Upperparts blackish-brown broadly edged grey. Coverts as upperparts, inners fringed whitish; outers wear quickly. Underparts as *SP* but with less streaking. Birds wintering in N. America moult July-October and in S. America August-January, so primaries are fresh in winter and slightly worn in spring.

Juv   As *Ad SP* but mantle with scaly chestnut pattern, and scapulars fringed whitish. Coverts brown broadly edged bright buff-brown, or chestnut on inners and tertials. Breast suffused buff and lightly streaked brown.

IW   As *Ad WP* but most birds retain *Juv* chestnut-fringed inner medians to spring; some appear to lose them. Primaries are slightly worn in midwinter, moderately worn by spring. Most in S. America moult outer primaries in spring, and possibly some have a complete moult.

IS   Only by retained inner medians and primaries moderately worn (northern winterers) or with contrast between old inners and new outers (southern winterers).

SEXING   ♀ averages larger. Bill length reported to give reasonable separation (65% of each sex): ♂ 15.8-18.6 (17.2), ♀ 17.2-21.0 (18.8). Practical separation by ⩽ 17.4 ♂, ⩾18.7♀.

GEOGRAPHICAL VARIATION   Possibly bill length decreases from east to west.

BIOMETRICS

Wing	21 A♂	86-94	(89.7)	: 25 J♂	86-94	(88.8)
	30 A♀	87-95	(92.1)	: 28 J♀	87-95	(90.9)
Bill	13 A	17-20	(18.5)	: 37 J	16-20	(17.9)
Tarsus	13 A	18-21	(19.1)	: 37 J	17-20	(18.4)

REFERENCES   Ident. 161, Age 14, Moult 106, 140, Biometrics 106, Weight 86, 97B.

WHITE-RUMPED SANDPIPER *Calidris fuscicollis*

NC N. Long-distance migrant.

IDENTIFICATION Small to medium-sized calidrid with blackish legs, and black bill with sometimes a yellow-brown tinge at base of lower mandible. From all smaller calidrids by white across upper tail coverts (rump), although this may be partly obscured. *C. ferruginea* is larger, with proportionately longer bill, neck and legs, and a wider white band across the upper tail. Fringed upperparts and strongly spotted breast and flanks in *SP* recall *C. mauri*, but larger and lacking bright rufous cap and ear-coverts. Bill also may resemble *C. mauri*, but always lacks distinct downturn at tip. Rather short narrow wingbar, wings when folded well overlapping tail.

AGEING

Ad SP Cap and ear-coverts brown/buff and chestnut, nape whitish with brown spotting, mantle blackish-brown edged chestnut, grey and buff. Coverts grey-brown, outers edged paler and inners fringed white. Underparts white, with breast and flanks spotted and streaked brown.

WP Upperparts fairly uniform brownish-grey, at first mixed with brown feathers. Coverts as *SP*. Underparts white, breast suffused and streaked grey-brown. Moult November-March, so primaries are fresh in spring.

Juv Mantle blackish-brown with bold chestnut, whitish and buff fringes. Coverts brownish with extensive buff and whitish fringes. Underparts white; breast and flanks suffused buff/grey with pale brownish streaks.

IW As *Ad WP* but grey and brown feathers mixed on mantle to midwinter. Some brownish inner medians with buff or cream fringes usually retained to spring. Moult is variable: some moult outers in spring, others possibly have a complete moult (if so are indistinguishable from *Ad*), but many appear not to moult primaries.

IS Only by worn primaries or replaced outers.

SEXING ♀ averages larger.

BIOMETRICS

Wing	29 A♂	120-129	(122.9)	: 12 J♂	119-125	(122.6)
	29 A♀	118-127	(124.2)	: 8 J♀	119-131	(123.7)
Bill	15 A♂	22-24	(22.8)	: 18 J	21-25	(22.8)
	19 A♀	23-26	(24.5)	:		
Tarsus	35 A	23-25	(24.2)	: 18 J	23-26	(24.3)

REFERENCES Age 14, Biometrics 155, Weight 86.

BAIRD'S SANDPIPER   *Calidris bairdii*

N N, also extreme NE P. Long-distance migrant.

IDENTIFICATION   Small to medium-sized calidrid with distinctly buff tone to all plumages. Very short and narrow wingbar; very little white at sides of dark rump. Wings when folded well overlapping tail. Bill black or greenish-black, similar to *C. fuscicollis* in shape and size but finer especially at tip. Legs rather short, blackish or greenish-black; toes rather short (middle toe only 16-19mm). Mantle appearing scaly in juveniles and *SP*, becoming dark brown tinged buffish in *WP*. Clear buffish-washed breastband in all plumages, brightest in juveniles and most streaked in *WP*.

AGEING

Ad SP Mantle grey-brown and black, with whitish and bright buff fringes and spots giving a variable blotched pattern. Coverts grey-brown; outers have slightly paler edges, and inners are fringed pale buff. Underparts white; breast buff-brown (sometimes greyish) with narrow dark brown streaks, sides of breast occasionally bright buff.

WP During September/October black on mantle is gradually replaced by grey-brown. Coverts grey-brown with very pale buff fringes; outers wear rapidly. Moult October-March, so primaries are slightly worn in autumn and fresh in spring. During moult fresh pale buff-fringed mantle and coverts are gained.

Juv Mantle blackish and grey-brown with extensive whitish-buff fringes forming a scaly pattern. Coverts grey-brown, tipped cinnamon-buff on outers and fringed chestnut-buff on inners. Underparts white, with breast buff indistinctly streaked brown.

IW Mantle fringes wear but usually visible to early November. Fringes on outer medians abrade and fade but bright buff fringes on inners are retained to midwinter; apparently outer coverts are replaced during winter, and inners in spring. Moult pattern not clear, but some birds do not moult, some moult outer primaries, and possibly others have a complete moult (these could not be told from *Ad*).

IS Only by moderately worn primaries, or contrast of old inners and fresh outers. May attain *SP*.

SEXING   ♀ averages slightly larger.

BIOMETRICS

				:			
Wing	21 A♂	119-131	(125.8)	:	18 J♂	122-131	(125.7)
	17 A♀	123-135	(128.3)	:	18 J♀	120-135	(125.9)
Bill	13 A♂	21-24	(22.4)	:	9 J♂	21-24	(22.4)
	10 A♀	22-24	(23.4)	:	8 J♀	20-24	(22.5)
Tarsus	25 A	21-24	(22.5)	:	25 J	21-24	(22.1)

REFERENCES   Biometrics, Weight 155.

PECTORAL SANDPIPER *Calidris melanotos*

NC and NE P, NW and NC N. Long-distance migrant.

IDENTIFICATION Medium-sized or medium-large calidrid (much individual variation in size). In all plumages by legs and base to bill greenish- or yellowish-brown, and heavily suffused and streaked neck and breast ending sharply against white lower breast and belly. Generally very dark above, with pale fringes in juvenile and *SP* forming lines on mantle; blackish rump and central upper tail coverts. Wing plain except for whitish tips to greater coverts and secondaries forming an indistinct wingbar and trailing edge. Narrow white sides to rump. Tail feathers 4-6 more or less equal in length and rather rounded at tip. Bill shortish, slightly decurved. Shares many characteristics with *C. acuminata* but is less rufous/buff, with different tail formula, clear division on lower breast, and narrow (about 1mm) white tips to primary coverts. *See Plate 6.*

AGEING

Ad SP Mantle and scapulars blackish-brown with variable chestnut and buffish fringes. Coverts grey-brown; outers with paler edges, and inners with whitish fringes. Underparts white, with heavily-marked breast and smudged flanks (for breast pattern see sexing).

WP Mantle grey-brown, coverts similar but paler at edge. (Beware: tertials have lateral buffish fringes but inner medians do not). Moult September-March, so primaries are fresh in spring and slightly worn in autumn.

Juv Mantle resembles *Ad SP* but brighter, with more whitish-buff especially on scapulars forming strong lines on back. Coverts with extensive buff fringes, palish on outers but almost chestnut on inners. Underparts white; breast streaked brown, with strong buff wash.

IW As *Ad WP* but inner medians darker brown and retaining buff fringes to spring. Primaries are slightly worn in midwinter, moderately worn in spring, very worn by late summer.

IS Only by very worn primaries.

SEXING *SP* ♂ breast feathers are blackish-brown with white spots at tip (breast appears slightly mottled); ♀ has breast whitish, streaked brown (as *WP* and *Juv*). ♂ with distendable gular sac in throat during breeding season.

size Almost no overlap in wing length of sexes: ≤ 135 ♀, ≥ 137 ♂. ♂ also with larger bill and tarsus.

BIOMETRICS

Wing	30 Ad♂	138-149	(144.2)	:	34 J♂	136-150	(143.0)
	20 A♀	126-135	(129.6)	:	30 J♀	124-136	(131.0)
Bill	29 Ad♂	27-32	(29.3)	:	29 J♂	26-31	(28.6)
	22 A♀	24-29	(27.4)	:	27 J♀	26-30	(27.4)
Tarsus	31 Ad♂	27-31	(28.8)	:	34 J♂	26-30	(28.4)
	20 A♀	25-28	(26.6)	:	30 J♀	26-28	(27.1)

REFERENCES Biometrics, Weight 155.

SHARP-TAILED SANDPIPER   *Calidris acuminata*

NE P. Long-distance migrant.

IDENTIFICATION   Medium-sized or medium-large calidrid, with legs and base to bill greenish- or yellowish-brown. Very similar to *C. melanotos* in structure and plumages, but is much brighter in *SP* and juveniles, and always lacks sharp border on the lower breast. Reddish cap, whitish supercilium and buff-washed breast are very distinctive especially in juveniles. Slightly whiter on primary shafts than *C. melanotos,* and with broader white tips (2mm+) to inner primary coverts. Tail wedge-shaped, with individual feathers rather pointed.

tail pattern

C. melanotos   C. acuminata

AGEING
Ad SP Mantle dark brown, edged pale chestnut and buff. Coverts grey-brown with paler edging. Underparts white; upper breast suffused pale chestnut-buff and fairly heavily spotted dark brown; brown V-shaped marks on lower breast and flanks.

WP   Upperparts brownish-grey. Coverts grey, with outers paler at edge and inners fringed whitish. Underparts white; breast finely and relatively sparsely streaked pale brown. Moult December-March, so primaries are fresh in spring, slightly worn in autumn.

Juv   Cap blackish broadly edged bright chestnut; mantle and scapulars blackish-brown fringed bright chestnut/buff/white; bold whitish supercilium. Coverts brown, extensively edged reddish-buff. Underparts with buff wash over all except lower belly; breast bright buff with a few brown streaks forming a gorget.

IW   As *Ad WP* but buff inner medians retained to midwinter, sometimes spring. Most moult outer primaries December-March, and so in spring have worn inner and new outer primaries, but a few may moult completely and some may not moult at all.

IS   Only on worn primaries or contrast of old inners and new outers; the few which have a complete moult are unageable. Most attain *SP*.

SEXING   Winglength provides 95% separation: ≤ 135 ♀, ≥ 136 ♂ . ♂ also has larger bill and tarsus. In *SP* ♂ has gular sac.

BIOMETRICS

Wing	14 A♂	136-145	(140.1)	: 37 J♂	133-145	(139.9)
	13 A♀	126-137	(131.2)	: 37 J♀	124-136	(130.2)
Bill	13 A♂	24-27	(25.4)	: 33 J♂	23-28	(25.7)
	14 A♀	22-26	(24.1)	: 34 J♀	22-26	(24.0)
Tarsus	16 A♂	29-32	(30.3)	: 37 J♂	29-32	(30.5)
	14 A♀	27-30	(28.5)	: 37 J♀	26-31	(28.3)

REFERENCES   Biometrics, Weight 155.

CURLEW SANDPIPER   *Calidris ferruginea*

NC and NE P (rarely NW N). Long-distance migrant.

IDENTIFICATION   Medium-sized calidrid, with characteristic longish tapering decurved black bill, and longish black legs. Also has white rump, although this may be partly obscured, and white wingbar. Chestnut-red head and underparts in *SP* recall larger *C. canutus*. Bill always more decurved and finer at tip than long-billed *C. alpina*, with lateral expansion almost lacking. Larger, with proportionately longer legs and bill than *C. fuscicollis* and a wider white band across upper tail coverts. Wingbar and black legs are best distinctions from *Micropalama himantopus*. See Plate 4.

AGEING

Ad SP Upperparts dark brown, broadly edged bright chestnut but tipped whitish or brownish-grey when fresh. Coverts grey-brown; outers tipped pale grey, whitish fringes to inners. Rump slightly obscured by dark bars. Whitish around bill, rest of underparts deep chestnut-red, in fresh plumage obscured by subterminal brown bars and/or broad whitish tips.

WP Upperparts grey-brown with many darker shaft streaks. Whitish supercilium. Coverts grey-brown with whitish-grey fringes. Underparts white; sparse grey-brown streaking on upper breast. Moult mostly September-February but in tropics may start in August, suspend for a variable period and complete November-March. Primaries are fresh in late winter and sometimes slightly worn in spring.

Juv Upperparts dark brown fringed pale buff, with a few chestnut edges. Coverts brownish, broadly fringed pale buff (tending towards chestnut on inners), with indistinct dark subterminal band. Underparts white suffused buff, with faint thin brown streaks on upper breast.

IW As *Ad WP* but *Juv* inner medians with rich buff fringes retained to February, sometimes later. Moult is variable but at least in E. and S. Africa they moult outer primaries (possibly they do not in NW Africa). In E. Africa there are two groups of moulters, February-April and May-June; in S. Africa moult is anytime February-August. Inner secondaries are also renewed. Thus in spring/summer there are contrasts in the primaries (old inners, new outers) and secondaries (new inners, old outers).

IS   Rarely any *Juv* coverts left. Usually by primary wear pattern (above). Virtually all remain south of breeding area and at most attain partial *SP*.

2W   Identifiable to early winter only on primary wear pattern, at first by worn inner primaries but, when these have been lost, by the worn outer secondaries which are replaced later.

SEXING   In *SP* ♀ has paler chestnut, more white feathers on underparts, and distinct brown bars on underparts. Also is slightly paler and whiter above. At all times bill length is helpful: almost all ⩽ 36 ♂, ⩾ 40 ♀, while in S. Africa only 10% of each sex is incorrectly identified by ⩽ 38 ♂, ⩾ 39 ♀.

BIOMETRICS

Wing	37 A♂	125-136	(131.0)	:	25 J♂	125-137	(130.6)
	20 A♀	125-136	(131.1)	:	22 J♀	127-138	(130.8)
Bill	35 A♂	33-39	(36.0)	:	26 J♂	32-44	(36.2)
	16 A♀	35-42	(39.4)	:	23 J♀	35-43	(38.7)
Tarsus	31 A♂	27-32	(29.3)	:	7 J♂	28-30	(29.0)
	15 A♀	29-31	(29.7)	:	7 J♀	28-32	(30.6)

REFERENCES   Age 114, Moult 26, 112, 120, 148, 153, 164, Sex 26, 146, Biometrics 26, 93, 125, Weight 26, 113, 141, 148.

PURPLE SANDPIPER   *Calidris maritima*

NC and NE N, NW and NC P. Resident or short- to medium-distance migrant.

IDENTIFICATION   Medium-sized calidrid with dark slate-grey or brownish plumage and dull yellow legs and base to bill. Legs rather short, bill longish and slightly decurved. White wingbar and trailing edge to secondaries; often one or two secondaries almost completely white. Very difficult to distinguish from some races of *C. ptilocnemis* (which see), but rather darker and less rufous above in *SP*, with less distinct blackish patch on lower breast; also white fringe to outer webs of inner primaries is narrower (about 1mm). *See Plate 6.*

AGEING

Ad SP   Cap blackish edged rufous; mantle and scapulars blackish with broken whitish-buff and chestnut fringes. Coverts dark brown, with outers fringed pale grey and inners whitish. Underparts white, with neck and throat streaked dark brown, and breast variably spotted blackish-brown (sometimes forming a small blackish patch on lower breast); flanks with some dark spots.

WP Head and neck uniform slate-grey; mantle and scapulars blackish-brown fringed grey and faintly glossed purple; coverts dark grey, edged paler on outers and fringed whitish on inners. Small whitish throat; upper breast slate-grey, lower breast mottled slate-grey/white with brownish streaks extending onto flanks. Moult July-September, primaries are fresh in winter, slightly worn by spring.

Juv Cap brownish edged pale chestnut; mantle and scapulars blackish-brown fringed chestnut and whitish. Coverts grey-brown with sharply defined broad pale buff fringes on outers, chestnut on inners and on tertials. Neck grey-brown, faintly streaked; breast streaked brown and mottled dark grey/brown/white.

IW As *Ad WP* but *Juv* chestnut- and buff-tipped inner medians and tertials retained to spring, while outer coverts fade to become whitish-fringed. Primaries are slightly worn in winter, moderately worn by spring.

IS Brownish *Juv* inner medians and tertials with buff fringes retained, although now are worn. Primaries moderately worn. Usually attain *SP*.

SEXING ♀ averages larger.

GEOGRAPHICAL VARIATION and BIOMETRICS (based on data supplied by R. C. Taylor). Two races described, nominate *maritima* and *groenlandica* (from Greenland), but there is little difference between them. There is a general decrease in wing, bill, tarsus and tail length both east and west of Iceland along 60°N.

Biometrics of breeding birds (means of samples 3-15)

		Iceland	N. Norway	Svalbard	E. Greenl.	W. Greenl.
Wing	♂	131.9	124.7	127.7	127.4	126.8
	♀	137.9	133.0	130.4	131.7	129.1
Bill	♂	28.3	27.0	26.7	27.9	26.7
	♀	33.6	31.9	30.8	31.4	30.9
Tarsus	♂	22.3	22.3	20.0	21.0	21.2
	♀	22.7	22.7	21.4	21.6	22.0

		Canada NWT	USSR (E)	USSR (W)
Wing	♂	129.4	—	127.6
	♀	132.0	132.6	132.6
Bill	♂	29.4	28.7	28.4
	♀	33.2	32.4	32.4
Tarsus	♂	22.0	20.0	20.9
	♀	23.0	21.3	21.3

REFERENCES Moult 96, Variation 78, Biometrics, Weight 2.

ROCK SANDPIPER   *Calidris ptilocnemis*

NE P and NW N. Resident or short-distance migrant.

IDENTIFICATION   The Pacific counterpart of *C. maritima*, distinct in some races but otherwise very difficult to distinguish. *C.p. ptilocnemis* is paler in *SP* and *WP*, with greenish legs, a well-defined blackish patch on lower breast in *SP*, and white on outer webs of inner primaries reaching shaft. Other races are more rufous above in *SP* than *C. maritima* (see table below), with better-defined blackish patch on lower breast, are slightly brighter in juvenile, and have white on outer webs of inner primaries about 2mm broad or more.

AGEING

Ad SP   Upperparts brownish-black edged chestnut and pale buff. Coverts brownish-grey with inners fringed white. Throat white; upper breast dark grey streaked blackish, lower breast usually with fairly extensive black patch; belly white.

WP   Upperparts fairly uniform mid-grey, at first with whitish tips. Coverts brownish-grey fringed white. Underparts white with upper breast blotched and suffused brownish-grey, some spots extending down flanks. Moult ends mid-September, so primaries are fresh in winter and slightly worn in spring.

Juv   Upperparts blackish-brown edged chestnut and whitish-buff. Coverts grey-brown, with outers broadly fringed pale buff and inners fringed chestnut. Underparts white; breast suffused buff and grey, lower breast and flanks streaked and spotted brownish.

IW   As *Ad WP* but buff-tipped inner medians and tertials retained to spring. Primaries are slightly worn in winter, moderately worn by spring.

IS   Sometimes have buff-tipped inner medians, but always with very worn primaries. Attain *SP*.

SEXING   ♀ averages larger.

GEOGRAPHICAL VARIATION and BIOMETRICS (based on data supplied by R. C. Taylor). Four races described:—*ptilocnemis* (Pribilof Is.), *tschuktschorum* (Chukotsk Peninsula, Alaska), *couesi* (Aleutian Is., S. Alaska), and *quarta* (Commander and Kuril Is.).

		C.p. ptilocnemis	*C.p.* tschukts.	*C.p.* couesi	*C.p.* quarta
Mantle redness					
	(amount)	least	medium	medium	most
	(shade)	palest	darkest	darkest	medium
Wing	♂	134.1	126.7	121.3	127.0
	♀	139.0	129.8	125.5	129.5
Bill	♂	30.4	26.7	26.8	25.8
	♀	34.7	31.0	29.8	29.6
Tarsus	♂	22.9	22.1	22.8	22.3
	♀	23.6	22.4	22.6	22.4

DUNLIN   *Calidris alpina*

N H, also MW P. Mainly medium-distance migrant.

IDENTIFICATION   Small to medium-sized calidrid, with considerable geographical variation in colour and size. Bill black, longish, with tip downcurved and slightly laterally expanded. Legs black. Clear white wingbar and sides to rump; grey sides to tail. Bill proportions sometimes similar to *C. mauri* but longer-billed than other small calidrids. Blackish spotting on flanks in juvenile and large black belly-patch in *SP* are clear features. Less buff than *C. bairdii*, with wing proportionately shorter and wingbar extending well onto primaries, and larger bill with broader tip. In *WP* can closely resemble *Limicola falcinellus*, which however has a broader bill and blackish lesser coverts. *See Plate 5.*

AGEING

Ad SP   Upperparts brownish-black, variably fringed pale to bright chestnut and whitish/grey. Coverts grey, outers paler at tip and inners fringed whitish. Black belly.

WP   Upperparts brownish-grey; coverts grey with whitish fringes, outers wear but inners retain fringes. Underparts white with breast streaked grey-brown. Moult is variable depending on race: *C.a. arctica* and *C.a. schinzii* usually migrate before moulting; *C.a. alpina* from the N.W. Palaearctic may start and suspend before migrating, or stop to moult during migration; N.E. Palaearctic and Nearctic birds moult on or near the breeding grounds before migrating. In general moult occurs July-October, so primaries are fresh in winter and slightly worn in spring.

Juv   Upperparts blackish-brown with whitish-buff and chestnut fringes. Coverts brownish with broad buff or chestnut fringes. Underparts white; breast streaked brownish, and flanks with fairly large blackish-brown spots.

IW   As *Ad WP* but chestnut/buff-fringed brown *Juv* inner medians are retained to summer. Primaries are slightly worn in winter, moderately worn by spring.

IS   Retained inner medians, but beware a small percentage of *IS* which apparently gain new inner coverts with a buff wash (these feathers might be retained into *2W*). Primaries moderately worn. Attain *SP*.

SEXING   *SP Ad* from Greenland, Europe and N.W. USSR can be sexed: ♂ has pale grey nape contrasting with cap and mantle, ♀ has nape streaked brownish and with little contrast. Both sexes of N.E. Palaearctic and Nearctic birds have pale collar. It is not possible to sex *Juv* or *WP* birds on present knowledge.

Size   Throughout range ♀ averages larger than ♂ but as there are clines in size it is rarely possible to sex individuals with certainty on measurements.

GEOGRAPHICAL VARIATION and BIOMETRICS (some of the moult and sexing data above and all the population biometrics presented below were supplied by Julian Greenwood — Ph. D. thesis *in litt.*). Six races are recognised:—*arctica* (N.E. Greenland), *schinzii* (Iceland, W. and S. Europe), nominate *alpina* (N.W. Palaearctic), *sakhalina* (N.E. Palaearctic, N. Alaska), *pacifica* (S. Alaska) and *hudsonia* (Canada). Some authors also admit *centralis* (central USSR) as an intermediate between *alpina* and *sakhalina*. Races differ as below.

A)   *SP characteristics of races*

	mantle fringes	breast streaking	belly patch
arctica	grey/white to buffish	faint	small
schinzii	yellowish-red	heavy	small
alpina	rich chestnut	heavy	large
(centralis)	rich chestnut	faint	large
sakhalina	deep rich chestnut	faint	large
pacifica	very bright chestnut	very faint	large
hudsonia	very bright chestnut	faint	large

B)   *Measurements (of breeding season birds)*

♂	wing		:	bill	
Greenland	107-117	(111.6)	:	23.2-29.3	(26.0)
Iceland	107-119	(113.1)	:	25.7-32.1	(28.7)
Britain	106-116	(110.8)	:	23.2-35.5	(27.7)
S.E. Baltic	105-118	(111.8)	:	24.5-32.4	(28.9)
S. Sweden	106-123	(112.2)	:	27.0-35.5	(28.4)
S. Norway	108-117	(112.7)	:	25.9-33.0	(28.1)
Lapland	112.5-119.5	(116.0)	:	27.1-33.3	(29.7)
W. USSR	111-118.5	(114.8)	:	29.1-33.3	(30.9)
C. USSR	109-117	(113.8)	:	28.7-34.5	(31.8)
E. USSR	113-125	(118.1)	:	30.3-36.5	(32.0)
S. Alaska	116-127	(121.3)	:	31.7-41.8	(36.6)
N. Alaska	116.5-126	(121.8)	:	30.1-39.8	(33.8)
Canada	115-127	(119.7)	:	33.0-41.4	(36.3)

♀	wing		:	bill	
Greenland	112-122	(115.5)	:	27.4-31.9	(29.5)
Iceland	111-122.5	(115.8)	:	27.8-34.6	(32.0)
Britain	109-121.5	(114.3)	:	27.1-34.0	(30.9)
S.E. Baltic	109-122	(114.2)	:	28.9-36.2	(32.0)
S. Sweden	111.5-123.5	(116.7)	:	30.8-39.1	(33.7)
S. Norway	110-120	(116.7)	:	27.8-36.1	(31.6)
Lapland	113-123	(118.1)	:	31.0-35.5	(33.7)
W. USSR	113-123	(117.4)	:	29.1-34.3	(32.7)
C. USSR	112-119	(115.5)	:	29.6-36.0	(34.2)
E. USSR	114-122	(119.0)	:	30.3-39.1	(35.1)
S. Alaska	120-131.5	(125.0)	:	36.9-43.7	(40.2)
N. Alaska	121-129	(125.1)	:	30.8-41.2	(36.6)
Canada	117.5-128	(121.9)	:	35.6-42.4	(39.0)

Tarsus length also varies considerably with Greenland ♂ x̄ 22.4, ♀ 23.5; W. Palaearctic ♂ x̄ 23.5-24.5, ♀ x̄ 24.5-25.5; and E. Palaearctic, Nearctic ♂ x̄ 25.5-27.5, ♀ x̄ 26.5-27.5.

REFERENCES Moult 6, 7, 39, 62, 63, 77, 107, 118, 120, Sex 83, 107, Variation 51, 79, 138, Biometrics 7, 27, 28, 39, 44B, 79, 82, 84, 94, 97, 103, 118, 138, 139, 160, Weight 7, 25, 39, 44B, 62, 83, 92, 94, 107, 118, 127.

SPOON-BILLED SANDPIPER
Eurynorhynchus pygmeus

NE P. Medium-distance migrant.

IDENTIFICATION Like a small calidrid but all ages including pullus have unique spatulate bill. In *SP* bright upperparts and chestnut-red head, neck and upper breast are very similar to *C. ruficollis*. Juvenile lacks bright rufous fringes and most resembles a miniature *C. alba*. In *WP* underparts are completely white recalling *C. alba* but upperparts are rather darker. White wingbar and sides to rump. Black bill and legs. *See frontispiece.*

AGEING

Ad SP Neck and face suffused with chestnut and streaked brown. Cap and scapulars blackish with rich chestnut edges; mantle edges slightly paler. Coverts grey-brown, inners fringed white. Underparts white, breast with much brown spotting and faint reddish wash.

WP Upperparts grey-brown; coverts grey, inners fringed white. Moult September-November, so primaries are fresh in winter, slightly worn in spring.

Juv Cap brownish with pale chestnut edges; nape very pale; mantle and scapulars brownish-black with white and buff edges; coverts brown, outers fringed pale buff and inners orange-buff. Underparts white; sides of breast washed buff, sometimes forming complete band, with slight lateral patches of brownish streaks.

IW As *Ad WP* but retain orange-buff inner medians to spring. Primaries are slightly worn in winter, and moderately worn in spring.

IS Some inner medians retained; primaries moderately worn. Usually attain at least partial *SP*.

SEXING ♀ averages larger.

BIOMETRICS Small sample, ages combined.

Wing	8♂	98-105	(101.0)	: 7♀	101-106	(104.0)
Bill	8♂	20-22	(20.7)	: 8♀	21-23	(22.2)
Tarsus	8♂	19-22	(20.1)	: 8♀	21-22	(21.1)

REFERENCES Biometrics 124.

BROAD-BILLED SANDPIPER   *Limicola falcinellus*

N P, (perhaps discontinuous). Medium- to long-distance migrant.

IDENTIFICATION Like a small to medium-sized calidrid, closely resembling *C. alpina* in *WP* but with bill distinctively broad from base to tip. *SP* and juvenile very dark with characteristic forked supercilium. In *WP* also from *C. alpina* by blackish lesser coverts recalling *C. alba*, poorer wingbar, and often by soft part colour. Bill longish, kinked downwards at tip, blackish or brownish, sometimes tinged green. Legs dark greyish-black, sometimes greenish or yellowish. *See Plate 7.*

C. alpina   bills from above   L. falcinellus

AGEING

Ad SP Upperparts blackish fringed pale chestnut to whitish, initially with broad grey-white tips; when worn becomes very black. Coverts brown, with inners fringed white. Underparts white; throat and upper breast heavily spotted with brown.

WP Upperparts darkish grey-brown with darker shaft streaks. Coverts as *SP*. Underparts white, with breast tinged and lightly streaked grey. Moult late August to December/January, so primaries are fresh in winter and slightly worn in spring.

Juv Upperparts blackish-brown with chestnut and whitish edges. Coverts palish brown, broadly edged with bands of pale buff. Breast faintly streaked dull brown.

IW Upperparts in winter blotched grey and brown. Buff edges to coverts fade rapidly so that, apart from buff-fringed inner medians, they resemble *Ad* by November. Inner medians and greaters are retained to spring. Primaries moderately worn by midwinter; outers are moulted March-May.

IS Contrast of worn inner and fresh outer primaries. Most attain *SP*.

SEXING ♀ averages larger in wing, bill and tarsus.

GEOGRAPHICAL VARIATION Two races recognised: nominate *falcinellus* (W. Palaearctic wintering E. to India) and *sibirica* (E. USSR, wintering Burma-China). They are separated with difficulty, but *sibirica* is slightly larger, in fresh *SP* with brighter yellow and white edges, and in *WP* slightly paler and greyer colour.

BIOMETRICS *L.f. falcinellus*

Wing	13 A♂	102-109	(104.8)	:	13 J♂	102-107	(104.1)
	17 A♀	103-114	(109.6)	:	21 J♀	104-114	(107.8)
Bill	11 A♂	28-33	(30.4)	:	13 J♂	27-33	(30.3)
	15 A♀	29-35	(33.2)	:	21 J♀	29-36	(33.2)
Tarsus	13 A♂	20-22	(20.9)	:	12 J♂	20-22	(21.2)
	17 A♀	20-22	(21.5)	:	21 J♀	21-23	(21.9)

L.f. sibirica

Wing	7 A♂	102-113	(107.4)	:	21 J♂	101-110	(106.5)
	11 A♀	108-115	(110.3)	:	20 J♀	105-114	(109.0)
Bill	9 A♂	27-34	(30.9)	:	21 J♂	26-33	(29.5)
	11 A♀	31-36	(32.7)	:	18 J♀	28-35	(31.8)
Tarsus	9 A♂	20-23	(21.7)	:	24 J♂	20-23	(21.2)
	11 A♀	21-23	(22.1)	:	20 J♀	21-23	(21.8)

REFERENCES Biometrics, Weight 27.

STILT SANDPIPER *Micropalama himantopus*

NC N. Long-distance migrant.

IDENTIFICATION Like a medium-sized to large calidrid but with long greenish or yellowish legs. Bill longish and decurved (like *C. ferruginea* but with broader tip), blackish with brownish base. No wingbar, but narrow white trailing edge to inner secondaries. White rump, although slightly obscured by barring in *SP*. Reddish ear-coverts and barred underparts are distinctive in *SP*.

AGEING

Ad SP Upperparts blackish with pale fringes, but by late August there are many grey feathers on mantle. Ear coverts and nape chestnut. Underparts white heavily barred dark brown/blackish.

WP Upperparts and coverts brownish-grey with white fringes, especially on inner medians. Underparts white. Moult is variable; some complete by October but most suspend, completing as late as February. Primaries are fresh in winter, slightly worn in spring.

Juv Upperparts blackish-brown with pale whitish/buff fringes. Coverts grey-brown broadly edged whitish-buff. Underparts whitish with buff wash on throat and upper breast and a few darkish streaks.

IW On upperparts, grey slowly replaces dark feathers, so throughout winter usually with some dark. Buff-fringed inner medians are retained to spring. Underparts white. Primaries slightly worn in winter, moderately worn by spring.

IS Retained *Juv* inner medians; moderately worn primaries. Some attain partial *SP*.

SEXING ♀ averages larger. In *SP* ventral barring of ♂ is blacker, while ♀ is more brownish. There is much overlap however.

BIOMETRICS

Wing	22 A♂	127-140	(131.6)	:	7 J♂	125-140	(132.6)
	14 A♀	131-139	(134.2)	:	8 J♀	131-134	(132.7)
Bill	22 A♂	37-42	(39.5)	:	7 J♂	37-42	(39.1)
	14 A♀	39-44	(41.9)	:	8 J♀	39-44	(41.0)
Tarsus	23 A♂	35-42	(39.4)	:	7 J♂	38-44	(40.6)
	15 A♀	39-45	(41.7)	:	8 J♀	41-46	(42.9)

REFERENCES Moult 67, Sex 66, 67, Weight 67, 86.

BUFF-BREASTED SANDPIPER
Tryngites subruficollis

NC N. Long-distance migrant.

IDENTIFICATION Like a medium to large calidrid, but with bill very short. Upperparts scaly with buff fringes, sides to rump buff. No clear wingbar. Underparts entirely buff, with white tips when fresh, and brown spotting at sides of breast. Underwing white but with rich buff lessers and black bar on under primary coverts. Remiges thickly spotted with blackish-brown distally, particularly on inner webs, contrasting strongly on undersides. Bill brownish-black, paler at base. Longish yellow legs. *See Plate 7.*

AGEING

Ad No distinct *SP*. Upperparts blackish with orange-buff edgings. Coverts with dark brown centre narrowing towards tip, and broad buff fringe; wearing during winter. Underparts warm buff; breast spots dark blackish-brown. Under primary coverts with striking broad black subterminal band. Underside of outer primary boldly spotted. Moult in winter, completing February-March.

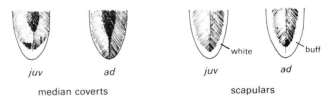

juv   ad   juv   ad

median coverts   scapulars

Juv Upperparts blackish-brown with whitish-buff edgings. Coverts with narrow brown centre, variably-sized brown subterminal band, and pale buff fringe. Breast spots paler brown than *Ad*. Underside of outer primary finely speckled; narrower black band on under primary coverts.

IW As *Ad* but coverts wear to leave dark subterminal band. In late winter primaries are moderately worn. Appear usually to have a complete wing moult in early spring—if so *IS* are similar to *Ad*.

SEXING ♂ larger; separable on wing length, ♂ ⩾ 134, ♀ ⩽ 132, and tarsus ♂ ⩾ 32, ♀ ⩽ 30.

BIOMETRICS

Wing	20 A♂	133-140	(136.6)	:	7 J♂	134-140	(136.9)
	19 A♀	124-132	(128.3)	:	3 J♀	129-130	(129.3)
Bill	16 A♂	19-21	(20.0)	:	6 J♂	19-20	(19.7)
	19 A♀	18-20	(18.6)	:	3 J♀	18-19	(18.7)
Tarsus	21 A♂	31-33	(31.9)	:	7 J♂	31-34	(32.1)
	19 A♀	27-31	(29.0)	:	3 J♀	28-29	(28.7)

RUFF   *Philomachus pugnax*

N and M P. Medium- or long-distance migrant.

IDENTIFICATION   Like a large long-legged calidrid or a large short-billed *Tringa*. Narrow white wingbar, conspicuous white sides to rump and especially to long upper tail coverts. Juvenile is buff below with scaly buffish pattern above; bill dark brown paler at base, and legs usually greenish- or yellowish-brown. Adults either in very distinctive *SP* or much greyer than juveniles; bill dark brown with orange-red, pinkish or yellowish base; legs usually orange-red or pinkish.

AGEING

Ad SP ♂ with unmistakeable variably coloured ruff and head tufts; ♀ lacks ruff and head tufts, but breast and mantle are mottled with blackish-brown feathers. Coverts grey-brown, paler at tips.

WP Upperparts grey-brown. Coverts grey-brown with paler edges; inner medians fringed whitish when fresh. Underparts whitish, breast streaked grey. Legs pinkish- or orange-red (all year). Moult August-January; timing is variable depending on latitude — later in Africa. Primaries fresh in winter, slightly worn in spring.

Juv Upperparts and coverts dark grey-brown with extensive warm buff edges. Underparts white, with breast washed buff and streaked brown. Legs usually yellowish-brown or greenish.

IW As *Ad WP* but with retained bright buff-fringed inner medians. Little contrast on coverts and mantle. Legs may become brownish-green or orange-green. Primaries slightly worn in midwinter, moderately worn by spring. A few (<10%) moult outer primaries February-May, and some may have a complete moult.

106

IS Many retain buff-fringed inner medians throughout the summer. Primaries either very worn or, less frequently, with contrast of old inners and fresh outers. Many ♂ attain a moderate degree of *SP* and return to breeding grounds, a few ♀ also. *IS* ♂ in *SP* has shorter pectoral ruffs (*IS* 49-91 mm *Ad* 66-98mm).

2W Until winter moult primary wear is a guide; coverts are *Ad* type, but leg colour is initially duller becoming steadily more orange-pink. Timing of leg colour changes is variable, with ♂ possibly becoming brighter earlier.

SEXING

SP ♂ unmistakeable with ruff and head tufts distinctive to late August. ♀ without ruff.

size At all seasons completely separated by wing length: ♂ > 175, ♀ < 170. ♂ also has larger bill and tarsus but there are small overlap zones.

BIOMETRICS

Wing	56 A♂	179-196	(188.7)	: 45 J♂	176-194	(186.0)
	25 A♀	151-162	(155.5)	: 44 J♀	148-167	(156.3)
Bill	53 A♂	31-39	(35.3)	: 44 J♂	31-37	(34.9)
	25 A♀	28-33	(30.6)	: 46 J♀	26-33	(30.4)
Tarsus	59 A♂	46-54	(50.5)	: 45 J♂	45-55	(49.5)
	24 A♀	38-44	(41.0)	: 47 J♀	37-45	(41.5)

REFERENCES Age 111, 134, 150, Moult 1, 111, 135, 153, Biometrics 1, Weight 1, 38, 113, 135.

NORMAN ARLOTT.

JACK SNIPE   *Lymnocryptes minimus*

N and MC P. Short- medium- or long-distance migrant.

IDENTIFICATION Shares longish bill, short legs, mottled rich brown plumage and creamy lines on crown and mantle with *Gallinago;* also has white trailing edge to secondaries and inner primaries. Much smaller and shorter-billed than *G. gallinago,* with green and purple glosses on back, scapulars and rump, and characteristic wedge-shaped tail of 12 pointed feathers. Bill dark brown, paler at base; legs pale greenish.

AGEING A very difficult species to age and the following comments are based on an as yet uncompleted study by A. O. Folkestad. The characters which appear to be of most use are:

Under tail coverts

Ad white with distinct blackish-brown subterminal patch spreading well onto the vane of the feather.

Juv whitish with indistinct yellowish-brown or greyish-brown subterminal shaft streaks. Apparently some are retained through the winter.

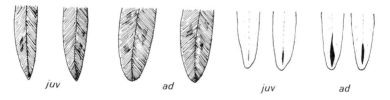

2nd and 3rd tail feathers   under tail coverts

Tail feathers

Ad feathers 2 and 3 relatively broad with rounded point. *Juv* 2 and 3 relatively narrow and finely pointed.

Other feathers, especially tertials scapulars and greater coverts, are also more rounded in *Ad* and more pointed in *Juv.* Leg colour is of some help, especially in autumn, as *Ad* is yellowish-green, and *Juv* greenish-grey. *Ad* moult July-September before migrating to wintering areas, but apparently there is little difference in wear between ages.

SEXING ♂ has longer wing on average.

BIOMETRICS

Wing	29 FG♂	110-121	(116.0) :	22 FG♀	107-119	(111.2)
Bill	26 FG♂	38-42	(40.3) :	19 FG♀	39-43	(40.7)
Tarsus	26 FG♂	23-25	(23.7) :	19 FG♀	23-25	(23.8)

REFERENCES Age 32, Biometrics, Moult 74.

COMMON SNIPE   *Gallinago gallinago*

N and M H. Resident or short- medium- or long-distance migrant (N).

IDENTIFICATION Rather variable species, very similar to Palaearctic *G. stenura* and *G. megala*, African *G. nigripennis* and S. American *G. paraguaiae*. From *G. stenura* and *G. megala* by clear white trailing edge to secondaries, at least 4mm broad on inner secondaries (and usually much broader in Palaearctic), and tail of 12-18 feathers (usually 14 or 16) with broad outers. *G. nigripennis* is much darker and more rounded-winged with tail recalling *G. media*, and *G. paraguaiae* has much narrower outer tail feathers and a more rounded wing. Smaller than *G. media*, with whitish ground colour only on outer tail feathers, more extensive white belly, and lacking bold white spotting on coverts. See also *G. hardwickii*. Bill dark brown, paler at base; legs pale greenish.

AGEING A difficult species, with ages similar throughout year but separable by:

Median/Lesser Coverts

Ad   distinctive dark shaft streak extending well onto vane (some, especially in winter, have a terminal black line). Coverts are renewed in autumn and spring but during winter and summer they fade and abrade; if the central streak is lost they resemble *Juv*. In winter have uniform wear of all coverts.

Juv   Fresh coverts have distinctive pale buff fringes and a black terminal line (which is rapidly lost). Some with thin central dark shaft streak but it hardly extends onto vane. Many are replaced by *Ad* type in autumn but some (especially inners) are retained, so that *IW* has contrast of worn *Juv* and fresh '*Ad*' coverts. The difference is clearest in *G.g. delicata*.

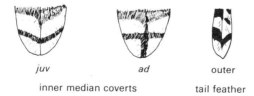

| juv | ad | outer |
| inner median coverts | tail feather |

Primary wear

Ad   Palaearctic birds moult July-August, so are fresh in winter and slightly worn in spring. Nearctic birds complete later, September-October, so have fresh primaries until late winter.

Juv   Slightly worn in early winter, moderately worn by spring.

SEXING Difficult especially in *G.g. gallinago* but in *G.g. delicata* there are differences as below (from Tuck):

109

Length of outer tail feathers (n=249): ≤43 ♀, ≥49 ♂ (but ♂ ≥47 in *SP*).
Bill (n=249): ≥70 ♀, ≤59 ♂; in overlap zone, ≤64 have sex ratio of 2 ♂—1 ♀ and ≥66 ratio 1 ♂ - 6 ♀.

GEOGRAPHICAL VARIATION   Three northern races are recognised: nominate *gallinago* (Palaearctic), *faeroeensis* (Faeroes, Shetlands, Iceland) and *delicata* (Nearctic). Faeroese *faeroeensis* are distinguished by very fine pale lines on back and scapulars, with the broader parallel lines almost absent, much less clear in Shetland and Icelandic birds. The others by:

	G.g. gallinago	*G.g. delicata*
number of tail feathers	typically 14	typically 16
width outer tail feathers (20mm from tip, *WP*)	typically ≥ 9mm	typically ≤ 9mm
white edge of secondaries	wide, ≥ 6mm	narrower, ≤ 5mm
axillaries	much more white than brown	more brown than white

BIOMETRICS   (races similar)

Wing	30 A♂	129-142	(136.0)	:	36 J♂	127-141	(134.6)
	23 A♀	129-141	(135.4)	:	44 J♀	128-141	(133.4)
Bill	27 A♂	60-70	(65.7)	:	33 J♂	55-74	(65.1)
	24 A♀	61-73	(68.0)	:	37 J♀	60-74	(66.3)
Tarsus	30 A♂	30-35	(31.6)	:	32 J♂	29-35	(31.7)
	23 A♀	30-34	(32.4)	:	40 J♀	28-36	(32.0)

REFERENCES   General 154, Age, Moult, Biometrics, Weight 102.

GREAT SNIPE   *Gallinago media*

NW, MW, NC and MC P. Medium- to long-distance migrant.

IDENTIFICATION   Adult distinguished from other snipes by bold white spotting on coverts, particularly greaters, outer medians and primary coverts, with a white bar formed by tips of greaters, and by all tail feathers except central pair extensively unbarred white at tip; these features are present but less clear in juvenile plumage. 14-18 tail feathers (usually 16), with outers relatively broad. Narrow white trailing edge to secondaries, about 2mm broad. Rather larger than *G. gallinago* (which see), with slightly shorter bill and unbarred area of belly less extensive.

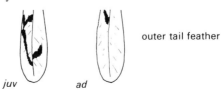

juv   *ad*   outer tail feather

AGEING

Ad   Median coverts boldly tipped white. Outer tail feather with distal 15mm or more clear white, then a small brown bar on outer web only. Moult is variable, apparently depending on latitude; some complete by October, but many suspend then and complete January-April. So in autumn show active moult with worn outers; in winter are either fresh or with fresh inners and moderately worn outers; in spring and summer are either slightly worn or fresh. The division at the point of a previous suspension is usually clear. Coverts are uniformly fresh in winter.

Juv   Coverts with relatively small white tips, partly obscured by buff (resemble worn *Ad* coverts). Outer tail feather white with fairly extensive brown marks extending to within 10mm of the tip on both webs.

IW   Most coverts and tail feathers replaced by midwinter; then from completed *Ad* by contrast of very worn and fresh coverts, but if all *Juv* coverts moulted may be unageable. Primaries slightly worn in early winter.

IS   Not identifiable for certain but probably have moderately worn primaries.

SEXING   ♀ averages larger, especially in bill length.

BIOMETRICS

Wing	49 Ao♂	142-154	(147.3) :	13 Jo♂	142-153	(147.5)
	23 A♀	145-155	(149.0) :	7 J♀	146-150	(148.3)
Bill	43 Ao♂	58-67	(62.1) :	13 Jo♂	56-64	(61.0)
	24 A♀	59-72	(66.7) :	7 J♀	61-69	(64.6)
Tarsus	52 Ao♂	35-39	(36.9) :	13 Jo♂	35-40	(37.0)
	27 A♀	36-40	(38.3) :	7 J♀	36-40	(37.7)

REFERENCES   General 154, Ident. 162.

PINTAIL SNIPE   *Gallinago stenura*

NC, MC and NE P. Medium-distance migrant.

IDENTIFICATION   Generally very similar to *G. gallinago* (which see) but has whitish tips to secondaries only about 1mm broad, and tail of 24-28 feathers (usually 26) of which the outer 6-8 pairs are extremely reduced to pin shapes only 1-2mm wide. Slightly smaller than *G. megala* and with different tail formula. Underwing coverts slightly more brown than white, as *G.g. delicata* and *G. megala,* but usually darker than *G.g. gallinago.*

111

AGEING   Ages very similar throughout year.

Ad   Lessers and medians with dark central shaft streak giving a rich buff-spotted appearance. In late summer coverts fade to resemble *Juv*, but are worn not fresh. After post-nuptial moult they go through a similar cycle and by late winter resemble retained *Juv* coverts, but now much fresher than those. Primaries with narrow indistinct whitish-buff tips. Moult appears to start in August, suspend September, and complete November. So in autumn inner primaries are fresh, outers moderately worn; in winter and spring all are fresh.

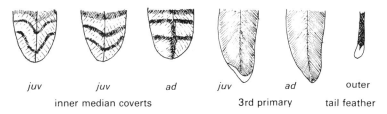

juv	juv	ad	juv	ad	outer
inner median coverts			3rd primary		tail feather

Juv   Lessers and medians with pale whitish-buff fringes; most are replaced by *Ad* type by early winter, but some very worn (almost lace-like) retained until early spring. Inner 8 primaries clearly tipped pale buff. Primaries are slightly worn in winter, moderately worn in spring.

SEXING   ♀ averages larger, especially in bill length.

BIOMETRICS

Wing	26 A♂	128-142	(133.7) : 27 J♂	130-138	(134.2)
	14 A♀	130-140	(136.4) : 19 J♀	130-138	(134.8)
Bill	25 A♂	56-64	(60.5) : 26 J♂	55-66	(60.3)
	14 A♀	59-69	(64.9) : 18 J♀	57-69	(62.9)
Tarsus	25 A♂	30-34	(31.1) : 26 J♂	30-35	(31.9)
	16 A♀	32-36	(33.3) : 20 J♀	29-35	(32.3)

REFERENCES   General 154, Ident. 80A.

SWINHOE'S SNIPE   *Gallinago megala*

MC and ME P. Medium-to long-distance migrant.

IDENTIFICATION   Very similar to *G. gallinago,* and particularly to *G. stenura,* but slightly larger. Narrow whitish trailing edge to secondaries, perhaps exceeding 1mm broad when fresh. Underwing similar to *G. stenura* but darker than most *G.g. gallinago.* Tail of 18-26 feathers (usually 20 or 22) with outers 2-4mm broad, narrower than *G. gallinago* but broader than *G. stenura.* Coverts often more clearly barred than in similar species.

AGEING

Ad Median coverts brown, barred and distally spotted dull buff, with clear central shaft streak. Tertials with bold clear buff/brown barring, lacking fringe. Moult inners early autumn, then usually suspend and complete October-November. Primaries are fresh in winter, slightly worn in spring.

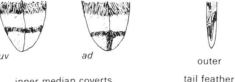

juv   ad   outer

inner median coverts   tail feather

Juv Median coverts brown with whitish-buff fringes. Tertials with large pale buff slightly mottled area and a whitish-buff fringe around distal third.

IW Some *Juv* median coverts retained for winter: these become very worn and contrast with fresh replaced *Ad* type feathers. Some buff-fringed tertials may be retained to late winter. Primaries are slightly worn in midwinter, moderately worn by spring.

SEXING   ♀ averages larger.

BIOMETRICS

Wing	10 A♂	137-150	(144.3) :	15 J♂	137-150	(142.6)
	7 A♀	143-147	(144.3) :	14 J♀	140-151	(144.7)
Bill	8 A♂	60-71	(63.5) :	15 J♂	56-65	(62.0)
	8 A♀	65-74	(67.9) :	13 J♀	62-72	(65.5)
Tarsus	11 A♂	32-36	(34.0) :	15 J♂	32-36	(33.4)
	8 A♀	33-38	(35.1) :	14 J♀	31-38	(34.5)

REFERENCES   General 154.

JAPANESE SNIPE   *Gallinago hardwickii*

ME P (Japan). Long-distance migrant.

IDENTIFICATION   A largish snipe, similar in plumage to previous four species but with proportionately long tail and wings, wings measuring 157mm or more. Most similar to *G. megala* in covert and underwing pattern and tail formula, but white trailing edge to wing is broader (2-4mm), and especially in juveniles inner primaries also are tipped whitish. Usually 18 tail feathers, outermost 4-6mm broad and next outermost 6-8mm.

AGEING

Ad Median coverts brown and buffish-brown with distinct dark shaft streak forming distal spots. Primaries indistinctly tipped palish, very indistinctly on middle ones. Moult completed late autumn/early winter, so primaries are fresh in midwinter and slightly worn in spring.

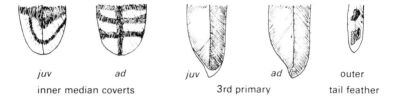

juv	ad	juv	ad	outer
inner median coverts		3rd primary		tail feather

Juv/IW Median coverts with distinct pale buff fringe; most are replaced by midwinter. Primaries with clearly defined white tips to most feathers. *IW* has complete moult starting December-January. Primaries are slightly worn in early winter, then in active moult but white-tipped (especially inner to middle) primaries can be recognised until replaced. Not identifiable for certain once moult is completed in spring but probably very fresh.

SEXING No characters found, but very few sexed birds in sample examined.

BIOMETRICS Sexes combined.

Wing	16 A	158-168	(163.1) :	21 J	157-165	(161.3)
Bill	17 A	66-77	(71.1) :	19 J	66-77	(70.9)
Tarsus	18 A	35-39	(36.4) :	21 J	34-39	(36.2)

REFERENCES General 154.

SOLITARY SNIPE   *Gallinago solitaria*

MC, SC and SE P. Resident or short-distance migrant. (O).

IDENTIFICATION Large and distinctively-coloured snipe, all ages with rather soft plumage. Generally gingery-brown, with whitish crown stripe and lines down mantle, lacking solid blackish feather centres and creamy-buff stripes of other species. Breast heavily suffused dull gingery-brown and mottled whitish; flanks barred brown leaving only a small clear white belly. Very narrow pale tips to primaries and secondaries, and white fringe to outer webs of outer 3 primaries. Tail strongly wedge-shaped, outer feathers 2-3mm broad and 20-30mm shorter than central pair, 16-28 feathers (usually 20).

AGEING Very difficult to age and no characters found for certain. Primary wear appears a possible character to late autumn (*Ad* slightly worn, *Juv* fresh), and in early winter *Ad* appear to be in suspended moult. Possibly a tendency for *Juv* to have more dark barring on belly, also *Juv* more frequently have dull chestnut patches on inner primaries and secondaries, and narrow edges to upperparts are slightly redder.

SEXING ♀ averages slightly larger.

GEOGRAPHICAL VARIATION Two races recognised: nominate *solitaria* (central Palaearctic wintering south to India) and *japonica* (SE Palaearctic wintering mainly in Japan). Very similar, but *japonica* has richer red and narrower white barring on back giving a less contrasting pattern. Sizes overlap but *japonica* has smaller wing and larger bill, see below:

	wing	*bill*	*tarsus*
G.s. *solitaria*	45,159-174(167.2) :	41,65-76(69.9) :	44,31-35(33.5)
G.s. *japonica*	25,157-171(162.4) :	25,67-78(72.9) :	25,33-36(34.0)

BIOMETRICS *G.s. solitaria* only, ages combined.

Wing	7♂	159-169	(165.9) : 16♀	163-171	(167.9)
Bill	5♂	68-72	(70.0) : 15♀	66-76	(70.5)
Tarsus	7♂	31-34	(33.0) : 16♀	32-35	(33.4)

WOOD SNIPE   *Gallinago nemoricola*

SE P. Short-distance migrant. (O).

IDENTIFICATION Largish snipe with dark plumage and heavily-barred belly. Rather rounded wings with narrow greyish tips to secondaries. Mantle blackish with lines usually grey-buff but sometimes rich brown-buff. In juvenile mantle is rather scaly, and primaries are also tipped pale. Underwing much more brown than white. Usually 18 tail-feathers, outers 3-4mm broad recalling *G. hardwickii* but with greyish ground colour.

AGEING

Ad   Most coverts dark brown with large grey-buff spots; inner medians with fairly wide grey-buff tips. Primaries fresh in winter, slightly worn in spring.

juv	ad	juv	ad
median coverts		inner median coverts	

Juv   Most coverts medium brown with warm chestnut-buff bars and pale buff terminal band, inner medians dark brown with narrow warm buff fringe. Primaries usually with clear white tips.

IW Coverts mostly replaced by *Ad* type, but retained inner medians wear to give two narrow lateral spots; they are often retained to *IS* but sometimes all are lost during winter. Primaries slightly worn in winter, moderately worn by spring.

SEXING Very few sexed birds examined.

BIOMETRICS Sexes combined.

Wing	9 A	146-153	(150.8) : 13 J	142-156	(147.2)
Bill	10 A	64-72	(68.2) : 12 J	61-71	(67.6)
Tarsus	9 A	35-39	(37.0) : 13 J	34-37	(35.8)

SHORT-BILLED DOWITCHER *Limnodromus griseus*

NW, NC and NE N. Medium-distance migrant.

IDENTIFICATION Snipe-like but with structure recalling small *Limosa*, and plumages chestnut-red or grey, and buffish in juveniles. Lower back white, rump and tail white barred dark brown. White trailing edge to secondaries and inner primaries, also variable white edges to outer webs of secondaries. Bill long and deep, recalling snipes, dark brown becoming paler and greener at base. Legs green or yellowish-green. *L. scolopaceus* is almost identical except in juvenile plumage, with differences as follows:—

(a) *Ad SP Scolopaceus* usually has belly chestnut-red in full plumage, and often distinct bars at sides of breast. The three races of *griseus* show slight differences (see Geographical Variation), but all have variable whitish or palish patch on lower belly, and sides of breast usually sparsely spotted (more intensely in the east).

griseus	*scolopaceus*	*griseus* *scolopaceus*	*griseus* *scolopaceus*
juv tertials		tail feathers	*juv* scapulars

(b) *Juvenile* Species quite easy to distinguish. *Griseus* has crown, back, scapulars and tertials dark brown broadly edged and vermiculated bright buff-brown. Subterminal dark area of feathers extends as a point down shaft, so worn feathers have buff-brown fringe broken by dark shaft streak. Submarginal markings clearly visible, especially on scapulars, and tertials often conspicuously tiger-striped. *Scolopaceus* has head, neck and upper breast much greyer; back, scapulars and

116

tertials dark brown with narrow fringe of chestnut-brown (darker than buff-brown of *griseus*) which on most feathers is scalloped. On worn and some fresh feathers, dark feather centre may break the fringe to give a line of spots around the edge. Submarginal markings virtually absent. Tertials rather plain with narrow edging. Diagnostic feathers conspicuous to at least November.

(c) **All plumages** Large overlap in bill measurements, with sexual differences and also racial differences in *griseus,* but most below 60 are *griseus* and most above 65 *scolopaceus.* Similarly tarsus, where most below 36 are *griseus* and most above 39 *scolopaceus.* Tail feathers have been quoted as a character but *griseus* are very variable and may show three patterns (barred with more brown than white, barred with more white than brown, and with brown longitudinal subterminal line on outer web) even within the same tail. In *scolopaceus* all feathers are more reliably fairly evenly barred with more brown than white. Under tail coverts are also very variable but in *griseus* the terminal brown mark tends to be a small spot or V, while in *scolopaceus* it is usually a complete brown bar or a bolder V.

AGEING

Ad SP Upperparts and some coverts blackish-brown marked rufous and pale buff; other coverts grey-brown with outers fringed paler and inners fringed white. Underparts reddish with whitish belly.

WP Upperparts and coverts uniform grey-brown; inner medians fringed white. Underparts white; neck and upper breast suffused pale grey-brown often with indistinct fine streaking. Moult late autumn-early winter, so primaries are fresh in winter, slightly worn in spring.

inner median coverts

juv   ad

Juv Coverts brown; outers tipped pale buff, inners chestnut. Neck and breast grey suffused buff (brightest on breast) and finely speckled brown; belly pale orange-buff.

IW As *Ad WP* but brown *Juv* inner medians with bright buff tips retained to spring. Primaries are fairly worn in midwinter, moderately worn by spring.

IS Usually only by very worn primaries. Some may attain *SP* but most remain south in *WP.*

SEXING ♀ averages larger, especially in bill length. It is not possible to sex individuals unless race can be determined, and even then there is much overlap.

GEOGRAPHICAL VARIATION   Three races recognised: nominate *griseus* (E. Canada), *hendersoni* (W. Hudson Bay — British Columbia), and *caurinus* (Alaska). Only differ in *SP* and size: *griseus* has a large white belly, extensive spotting on all of breast and most dark on tail; *hendersoni* has pale cinnamon belly, sparse spotting on breast and belly, most white in tail; *caurinus* is intermediate in colour with small white belly. Increase in size (wing, bill and tarsus) from east to west, but with much overlap.

BIOMETRICS   (Small sample, races combined).

Wing	21 A♂	142-152	(147.8) :	24 J	139-153	(146.0)
	11 A♀	150-156	(152.2) :			
Bill	19 A♂	51-64	(57.4) :	24 J	53-67	(56.4)
	11 A♀	59-65	(61.9) :			
Tarsus	21 A♂	32-37	(35.2) :	23 J	31-39	(35.1)
	11 A♀	34-37	(36.2) :			

REFERENCES   Ident. 101, 122, Variation 122, 132, Biometrics 101, Weight 86.

LONG-BILLED DOWITCHER

Limnodromus scolopaceus

NE P and NW N. Medium- to long-distance migrant.

IDENTIFICATION   Often very difficult to tell from *L. griseus* (which see), but is slightly larger and longer-billed, and has distinct juvenile plumage. Calls also differ and are useful for identification. *See Plate 9.*

AGEING and moult as *L. griseus.*

SEXING   ♀ averages larger; bill length, ≤ 65 ♂, ≥ 67♀.

BIOMETRICS   (few sexed birds examined).

Wing	18 A	146-159	(151.1) :	22 J	140-159	(151.0)
Bill	19 A	57-77	(65.2) :	★J♂	54-66	(61.8)
				♀	66-78	(71.8)
Tarsus	19 A	34-42	(38.4) :	★J♂	35-40	(37.8)
				♀	38-45	(41.1)

★ from Nisbet (1961) after Pitekla (1950).

REFERENCES   Ident. 101, 122, Variation 122, 132, Biometrics 101.

ASIATIC DOWITCHER   *Limnodromus semipalmatus*

MC and ME P. Medium- or long-distance migrant.

IDENTIFICATION   Larger than other *Limnodromus*, and with structure and plumages recalling *Limosa lapponica baueri*. From *Limosa* by long deep straight bill conspicuously swollen at tip, and smaller size. Back dark, rump and upper tail coverts white barred brown, tail largely dark. No clear white trailing edge to wing, but greaters, secondaries and inner primaries with white outer edges. Bill black, slightly brownish at base. Legs grey-black.

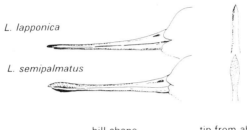

L. lapponica

L. semipalmatus

bill shape   tip from above

AGEING

Ad SP Mantle and scapulars brownish-black with chestnut edges, back of neck often noticeably chestnut. Coverts grey-brown, fringed white. Underparts chestnut, with some whitish on belly.

WP Upperparts dark grey-brown, coverts as *SP*. Underparts whitish with neck, breast and flanks mottled and barred pale brown. Moult late August-November, so primaries are fresh in winter, slightly worn in spring.

Juv Upperparts uniform brownish with mantle and scapulars narrowly edged buff. Coverts light brown with pale buff edges. Underparts white with breast, upper flanks and neck strongly washed warm buff.

IW As *Ad WP* but buff-edged inner medians retained to January, sometimes also scapulars to December. Primaries slightly worn by early winter, moderately worn in spring.

IS Apparently only by moderately worn primaries.

SEXING ♀ averages larger and appears slightly duller in *SP*.

BIOMETRICS   (few sexed birds examined)

Wing	18 FG		174-188	(179.1)			
Bill*	FG ♂		75-82	(80.1) : FG ♀	78-87	(82.9)
Tarsus*	FG ♂		46-53	(50.7) : FG ♀	48-54	(50.8)

* data from Nisbet (**1961**) after Pitelka (**1950**).

REFERENCES   Ident. 101.

WOODCOCK   *Scolopax rusticola*

M P. Resident or short- to medium-distance migrant.

IDENTIFICATION   Large snipe-like wader, most resembling *Gallinago nemoricola* but larger, with short reddish-flesh legs, transverse bars on hind-crown, strongly vermiculated upperparts admixed with grey, and silver-grey terminal spots to underside of tail feathers. Bill fleshy-brown, darker at tip. From much smaller *Philohela minor* by barred underparts, darker mantle, and longer wing with outer primaries not reduced.

AGEING   *Ad* and *Juv* fairly similar, separated by the following characters (after Clausager 1973):

Primary wear Ad moult July-September, so are fresh in winter, slightly worn in spring/summer. *Juv* are slightly worn in early winter, moderately worn in spring, and very worn by second autumn.

primary coverts

juv   *ad*

Primary coverts Ad narrow (≤1.0mm) distal fringe which is paler than rest of spots on that covert. *Juv* broad (≥1.5mm) distal spots which are same colour as rest of spots on that covert.

Tail feathers Ad distal spot clear silvery-white, general colour dark brown with small clear paler patches. *Juv* distal spot dull greyish-white, general colour paler brown often with extensive indistinct mottling. Feathers shorter than *Ad*. These differences are not always easy to see, and feathers replaced during *IW* are of *Ad* type.

SEXING   Large overlap in measurements, but ♂ has longer tail and shorter bill, therefore ratio of tail/bill length useful. In *Ad*, ≤1.10 ♀, ≥1.20 ♂ (sexes 45% of birds). In *Juv/IW* ≤1.00♀, ≥1.20 ♂ (sexes 24% of birds).

GEOGRAPHICAL VARIATION   Almost none but sedentary population on Ryu Kyu Is. (S. Japan) often separated to specific level — *Scolopax mira* (Amami Woodcock). It is much redder than most *S. rusticola*, with no grey. The wing and bill lengths are in *S. rusticola* range but tarsus is much longer (44 and 45 in the only two specimens examined) and thicker. Ageing criteria are probably similar to *S. rusticola*.

BIOMETRICS

Wing	13 A♂	195-206	(199.5) : 27 J♂	189-205	(197.5)
	8 A♀	185-202	(195.6) : 18 J♀	189-204	(196.8)
Bill*	115 A♂	64-80	(71.5) :136 J♂	63-77	(70.8)
	90 A♀	63-81	(74.7) :130 J♀	65-83	(74.3)
Tarsus	13 A♂	34-37	(35.1) : 27 J♂	32-39	(34.8)
	9 A♀	34-37	(35.6) : 21 J♀	31-39	(35.4)
Tail*	95 A♂	78-96	(85.9) : 83 J♂	68-93	(82.0)
	64 A♀	77-88	(82.4) : 57 J♀	66-86	(80.0)

* from Clausager (1973).

REFERENCES General 137A, Age, Sex, Biometrics 17.

AMERICAN WOODCOCK *Philohela minor*

MC, ME, SC and SE N. Resident or short-distance migrant.

IDENTIFICATION Shares bulky proportions, transverse bars on hind crown, vermiculated upperparts, and silver-grey terminal spots to underside of tail feathers with *S. rusticola*, but is much smaller and has entire underparts unbarred orange-buff. Upperparts brighter, including orange-brown and clean grey. Outer 3 primaries greatly reduced in width and length, primaries 6 and 7 longest.

AGEING Plumages similar, separable by:—

Pattern on underside of tip of middle 4 secondaries
Ad have dullish patterning, with only slight contrast between distal light brown area and buffish subterminal zone. *Juv/IW* have clear white tip and contrasting dark brown subterminal zone, usually with clear dark point in centre. By *IS* white is usually lost but much of dark zone remains.

middle secondaries

juv   *ad*

Primary wear *Ad* moult late June-mid October, so primaries are fresh in midwinter, slightly worn in spring. In *Juv/IW* primaries are slightly worn in winter, moderately worn by spring.

SEXING ♀ averages larger than ♂. Although in large samples there is slight overlap, in our small sample there was complete separation.

	wing	*bill*	*tarsus*	*width of 8th primary*
♀	≥140	≥70	≥33	≥5.0
♂	≤134	≤69	≤31	≤4.6

Also Sheldon (1967) gives weight separation:—summer ♂ 125-167g., ♀162-215; winter means ♂ 156, ♀ 200.

BIOMETRICS Small sample, ages combined.

Wing	16♂	128-134	(130.2)	: Tarsus	16♂	29-31	(30.4)
	10♀	140-146	(143.7)	:	10♀	33-35	(33.9)
Bill	15♂	62-69	(65.0)	: 8th pri-	16♂	3.4-4.6	(4.0)
	10♀	70-73	(72.2)	: mary width	10♀	5.0-6.2	(5.4)

REFERENCES General 136, Age 81, Moult 105, Sex, Biometrics 81, Weight 105.

NORMAN ARLOTT

BLACK-TAILED GODWIT   *Limosa limosa*

M P. Short- medium- or long-distance migrant.

IDENTIFICATION   Large, long-legged, long-billed wader. From other godwits except *L. haemastica* by white wingbar, and contrast of dark upper rump, white lower rump, upper tail coverts and base of tail, and mainly black distal tail. From *L. haemastica* by bolder wingbar (outer webs of some inner secondaries extensively white), broader white across lower rump and upper tail coverts, and white underwing and axillaries. Belly always white in full *SP*, but beware ♀ *L. lapponica*. Bill nearly black distally, basal half pinkish-flesh, or bright orange in *SP*. Legs dark greyish. *See Plate 8.*

AGEING

Ad SP   Upperparts a mixture of grey-brown and blackish-brown with rufous-buff fringes. Coverts grey-brown, fringed whitish on inners. Underparts with variable amount of red and dark brown barring, depending on sex and race.

WP   Upperparts and coverts uniform pale grey-brown; inner medians fringed white. Underparts white, with breast washed brownish. Moult July-October, so primaries are fresh in winter, slightly worn in spring.

Juv   Upperparts darkish brown with pale chestnut and whitish edgings. Coverts brown with reddish-buff fringes. Neck and breast reddish-buff, belly white.

IW   As *Ad WP* but some buff-fringed brown inner medians are retained, in the north until spring but in Africa often all are lost by midwinter. Primaries slightly worn in winter, moderately worn by spring. In *L.l. melanuroides* has darker breast than *Ad*.

IS   Primaries very worn; most commence moult May/June. Some attain partial *SP*.

SEXING   Possible to sex birds (if in full *SP* and race is known) by colour of underparts and by bill length. In *SP Ad* ♂ is much more red and with brown bars on underparts; *Ad* ♀ often has very little chestnut and few brown bars. ♀ has longer bill (also tarsus and wing, but more overlap with these characters).
  Bill length of W. European adults *L.l. islandica* ≤84♂, ≥86♀: *L.l. limosa* ≤94♂, ≥104♀.

GEOGRAPHICAL VARIATION and **BIOMETRICS**   Three races recognised: *islandica* (Iceland), nominate *limosa* (rest Europe, W. Asia) and *melanuroides* (E. Asia). In *SP Ad* ♂ *islandica* and *melanuroides* are extensively darkish red on underparts; *limosa* has red more cinnamon in shade and it rarely extends past lower breast. *Ad* ♀ shows same trend but with less red. In *WP melanuroides* has dark grey-brown upperparts but other two are paler. In *Juv* plumage *islandica* has much richer chestnut-buff neck and breast than *limosa*.

123

Nominate *limosa* shows a clinal increase in size from W to E, while the other two races are much smaller. The range, (mean) and sample size of four groups of *Ad* are set out below (*limosa* and *melanuroides* supplied by S. Rynn).

		L. l. islandica	*L.l. limosa* W. Europe	E.Europe/W. Asia	*L.l. melanuroides*
Wing	♂	201-218 (208) 6	193-228 (207) 52	188-217 (207) 15	168-210 (184) 28
	♀	207-240 (216) 9	205-231 (219) 33	201-230 (218) 8	180-209 (195) 15
Bill	♂	74-85 (79) 6	80-123 (91) 48	79-107 (96) 15	67-88 (75) 29
	♀	85-100 (91) 9	95-117 (107) 33	100-122 (109) 8	73-93 (82) 15
Tarsus	♂	60-75 (67) 6	64-96 (73) 53	67-91 (77) 17	59-70 (63) 30
	♀	71-76 (74) 9	73-88 (81) 33	75-88 (82) 8	62-73 (68) 16

REFERENCES Moult 120, Sex 53, Variation 50, 158, 167, Biometrics 34, 35, 53, 72, 117, Weight 117.

HUDSONIAN GODWIT *Limosa haemastica*

NC N. Long-distance migrant.

IDENTIFICATION Similar to *L. limosa* and with white wingbar and similar tail pattern, but told by narrower wingbar (not showing beyond coverts on secondaries), narrower white band across upper tail coverts, and axillaries and most of underwing black. Chestnut-red in SP extends to belly and under tail coverts, as in ♂ *L. lapponica,* but more heavily barred and with throat whitish.

AGEING

Ad SP Upperparts blackish, pale chestnut and buff fringes wearing off rapidly. Coverts grey-brown, with small whitish fringes on inners. Underparts red with dark brown and some white barring.

WP Upperparts uniform grey-brown. Coverts grey-brown, with inners fringed white. Underparts whitish but grey-brown wash on upper breast and neck. Moult September to November/December, so primaries are fresh in winter, slightly worn in summer.

Juv Upperparts brownish-black, fringed buff/whitish; coverts brown, fringed buff. Tertials and scapulars broadly barred buff and brown. Underparts buffish.

IW As *Ad WP* but *Juv* buff-fringed inner medians retained to spring. Primaries moderately worn by late winter/spring.

IS   Primaries very worn; some *Juv* inner medians still present. Some may attain full *SP*.

SEXING   In *SP* ♂ tends to be much brighter with more extensive red, and brown bars sometimes tipped white; ♀ is sometimes quite red but with white bases to feathers. ♀ usually has paler mantle. Fairly good separation on bill and tarsus length:—

A♂   bill ⩽84 and tarsus ⩽66 : J♂   bill ⩽80 and tarsus ⩽58
A♀   bill ⩾85 and tarsus ⩾67 : J♀   bill ⩾83 and tarsus ⩾60

BIOMETRICS   (adults per S. Rynn)

Wing	49 A♂	200-219	(207.5) :	9 J♂	201-210	(205.3)
	31 A♀	203-229	(218.5) :	9 J♀	209-216	(213.2)
Bill	49 A♂	69-84	(75.4) :	9 J♂	64-80	(74.0)
	31 A♀	74-96	(88.6) :	9 J♀	83-93	(88.9)
Tarsus	49 A♂	52-66	(56.9) :	8 J♂	52-58	(54.1)
	31 A♀	54-72	(62.5) :	9 J♀	60-64	(61.8)

BAR-TAILED GODWIT   *Limosa lapponica*

N P and NW N. Medium- to long-distance migrant.

IDENTIFICATION   From other godwits by white ground colour and brown bars on rump and upper tail coverts (lower back also white in *L.l. lapponica*). No clear wingbar, but secondaries edged white. Tail brown, usually obscurely barred. Entire underparts largely unbarred chestnut-red in *SP* ♂. Underwing and axillaries white barred brown, heavily in *L.l. baueri*. Slightly smaller than *L. limosa* on average and rather shorter-legged. Resembles *Limnodromus semipalmatus* but is larger and has tapering slightly upturned bill with pinkish or orange base. *See Plate 8*.

AGEING

Ad SP   Upperparts blackish-brown with reddish notches. Coverts grey-brown, paler towards edges. Underparts variable, see sexing.

WP   Upperparts grey-brown with darker shaft streaks. Coverts brownish-grey; outers paling towards tip, inners fringed white. Tertials greyish with thin whitish edges. Central tail feathers with large irregular grey-brown area. Underparts whitish, with sides of breast slightly streaked brown. Moult August-December (tends to be later in *baueri*), so primaries are fresh in winter and slightly worn in summer.

Juv   Upperparts brown with broad buff borders. Coverts brown, with buff fringe interrupted centrally at tip by a wedge of brown. Tertials as coverts but buff fringe composed of a series of joined spots. Central tail feathers white, strongly barred brown. Underparts whitish, with breast strongly washed buff.

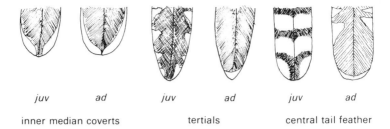

juv	ad	juv	ad	juv	ad
inner median coverts		tertials		central tail feather	

IW As *Ad WP* but some *Juv* inner medians, tertials and central tail feathers remaining. Although wear is rapid, the patterns are still discernible through to spring. Primaries are slightly worn in winter, moderately worn by spring.

IS Very worn primaries; moult July–September. Most do not attain full *SP*.

SEXING ♀ larger. Best separated by bill length, but a few intermediates will not be sexable.

L.l. lapponica	$Ad \leqslant 85 \, \text{♂}, \geqslant 88 \, \text{♀} : Juv \leqslant 74 \, \text{♂}, \geqslant 84 \, \text{♀}.$
L.l. baueri	$Ad \leqslant 99 \, \text{♂}, \geqslant 100 \, \text{♀} : Juv \leqslant 89 \, \text{♂}, \geqslant 91 \, \text{♀}.$

Juveniles have more overlap. ♀ is also larger in wing and tarsus.

In *SP* ♂ has underparts all bright chestnut-red, while ♀ is usually pale pink-chestnut and grey on breast, often barred or spotted brown. Sometimes *SP* almost absent in ♀.

GEOGRAPHICAL VARIATION Two races recognised: nominate *lapponica* (Scandinavia, W. USSR) and *baueri* (E. USSR, Alaska). Differ in colour of axillaries and rump/lower back: *lapponica* has white axillaries narrowly barred brown, and a white rump and lower back sparsely marked with brown; *baueri* has brown axillaries narrowly barred white, and a much darker rump although with some white on lower rump and uppertail coverts. There is complete intergradation between them, and intermediates have been given the name *menzbieri*. Eastern population *(baueri)* is noticeably larger, but plumage is the easier character.

BIOMETRICS *L.l. lapponica*

Wing	64 A♂	200-221	(211.3)	:	57 J♂	190-219	(204.7)
	31 A♀	214-231	(223.3)	:	31 J♀	209-224	(216.9)
Bill	62 A♂	69-87	(78.5)	:	54 J♂	61-83	(75.0)
	30 A♀	86-108	(99.2)	:	37 J♀	75-103	(90.0)
Tarsus	65 A♂	46-53	(50.0)	:	57 J♂	47-55	(50.3)
	28 A♀	52-59	(55.4)	:	39 J♀	51-61	(54.3)

L.l. baueri

Wing	26 Ao⁷	210-242	(224.4)	:	17 Jo⁷	199-228	(211.9)
	17 A♀	227-256	(238.9)	:	14 J♀	216-240	(227.1)
Bill	26 Ao⁷	75-94	(83.6)	:	12 Jo⁷	72-88	(79.4)
	15 A♀	102-119	(110.5)	:	14 J♀	96-116	(100.9)
Tarsus	27 Ao⁷	48-58	(53.6)	:	18 Jo⁷	50-56	(52.3)
	15 A♀	55-63	(59.3)	:	15 J♀	52-61	(57.2)

REFERENCES Age 30, Moult 6, 44A, Sex 44A, Variation 123, Biometrics 44A, 117, Weight 30, 44A, 92, 117.

MARBLED GODWIT   *Limosa fedoa*
MC N. Short- or medium-distance migrant.

IDENTICATION Like a large *L. lapponica* but with dark back and rump and much cinnamon in plumage. Axillaries and underwing rich cinnamon-brown; secondaries, inner primaries and tail also largely cinnamon-brown, lightly barred and spotted brown; only primaries 7-10 dark. Upperparts including rump brown, heavily barred and spotted buff-brown or cinnamon-buff. Underparts cinnamon-buff, narrowly barred or marbled brown in *SP*. *Numenius americanus* has similar colours but is much larger with a very long decurved bill.

AGEING

Ad SP Upperparts blackish edged chestnut and warm buff. Coverts edged warm buff-brown. Upper neck whitish; rest of underparts rich cinnamon-buff with brown bars on breast and flanks.

WP Median coverts edged pale buff-brown to chestnut. Underparts dull cinnamon with very little barring. Moult July-November, so primaries are fresh in winter, slightly worn in spring.

Juv Median coverts buff-brown, broadly edged pale buff. Underparts uniform cinnamon-buff with a few bars on flanks.

IW Median coverts fade to almost white by November and in winter can be difficult to identify; often are replaced by spring. Primaries are moderately worn by winter, very worn in spring.

IS Very worn primaries.

SEXING ♀ averages significantly larger in all measurements.

BIOMETRICS (per S. Rynn)

Wing	55 Ao⁷	217-245	(228.9)	:	10 Jo⁷	205-244	(221.6)
	40 A♀	218-255	(239.9)	:	20 J♀	219-245	(233.5)
Bill	55 Ao⁷	82-122	(96.6)	:	10 Jo⁷	87-114	(96.3)
	40 A♀	90-130	(114.6)	:	20 J♀	96-126	(114.4)
Tarsus	55 Ao⁷	60-77	(70.4)	:	10 Jo⁷	62-81	(69.4)
	40 A♀	67-82	(75.3)	:	20 J♀	61-83	(75.4)

LITTLE WHIMBREL   *Numenius minutus*

NC and NE P. Long-distance migrant.

IDENTIFICATION   Very small curlew with dark crown and narrow pale
crownstripe. Much smaller than other *Numenius* except *N. borealis*, from which
by slightly smaller size, more buff and less cinnamon in plumage, whitish belly
with less streaking on breast and flanks, and underwing and axillaries buff with
brown barring. Rump dark brown barred and spotted buff, as mantle. Bill
decurved, but very short for *Numenius*, dark brown paling to fleshy or yellowish
at base. Legs bluish-grey, whole tarsus scutellated. Sometimes regarded as
conspecific with *N. borealis*.

AGEING

Ad   (only *SP* examined). Scapulars have large buff spots; coverts are
narrowly edged with distinct spots of buff. Primaries without or with
only very narrow pale edging at tip. Based on wear, moult appears to take
place late autumn-late winter; primaries fresh in spring.

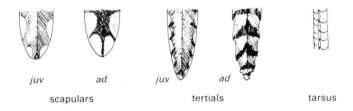

juv   ad   juv   ad

scapulars   tertials   tarsus

Juv/IW Scapulars with small narrow whitish-buff spots on edges, wearing off
by November. Coverts broadly edged and indistinctly spotted buff.
Primaries 1-6 with noticeable whitish tips. Some renew outer primaries
in spring.

IS   Apparently only by worn primaries, or by contrast of old inners and new
outers.

SEXING   ♀ averages larger.

BIOMETRICS

Wing	4 A♂	177-187	(181.7)	:	6 J	183-187	(185.5)
	8 A♀	185-193	(188.1)	:			
Bill	6 A♂	40-48	(43.5)	:	6 J	41-45	(43.5)
	8 A♀	40-48	(44.6)	:			
Tarsus	6 A♂	47-51	(49.0)	:	6 J	46-51	(49.3)
	7 A♀	49-51	(50.0)	:			

ESKIMO CURLEW

Numenius borealis

Formerly N N, long-distance migrant; now extremely rare (perhaps extinct).

IDENTIFICATION Very small curlew with dark crown and rather indistinct pale crownstripe. From *N. minutus* by cinnamon tone above, and whole underparts washed cinnamon with heavier streaking and barring on breast and flanks (often Y-shaped marks). Also slightly larger and longer-billed, with underwing and axillaries bright cinnamon with brown barring. Very much smaller than *N. americanus,* which also shows cinnamon. Bill blackish-brown paling to fleshy at base. Legs bluish-grey, reticulated posteriorly. Sometimes regarded as conspecific with *N. minutus.*

AGEING

Ad Tertials and scapulars boldly spotted or barred brown/buff; wear rapidly and are very abraded by late autumn. Coverts edged and notched buff when fresh, but by autumn with very narrow pale edges. Primary coverts wholly dark, or tipped white. Moult late autumn-late winter; primaries are fresh in spring, slightly worn in autumn.

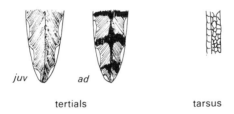

tertials   tarsus

Juv/IW Tertials and scapulars with narrow pale buff edges and small spots; by winter pale edges wear off to leave uniform, slightly notched feathers. Coverts with more extensive buff edges and spots than *Ad.* Primary coverts tipped buff; primaries 1-7 tipped whitish, especially on inner web. Primaries slightly worn in winter, moderately worn by spring.

IS Primaries very worn.

SEXING ♀ averages larger.

BIOMETRICS

Wing	4 Ao'	205-220	(214.0)	:	5 Jo'	187-218	(206.2)
	4 A♀	215-226	(222.2)	:	5 J♀	199-217	(207.4)
Bill	3 Ao'	48-52	(50.3)	:	5 Jo'	44-53	(50.2)
	2 A♀	54-58	(56.0)	:	5 J♀	42-57	(49.6)
Tarsus	4 Ao'	42-43	(42.7)	:	4 Jo'	42-46	(44.0)
	4 A♀	44-46	(44.7)	:	5 J♀	42-45	(43.8)

WHIMBREL   *Numenius phaeopus*

NW and NE P, NW and NC N. Medium- or long-distance migrant.

IDENTIFICATION Medium-sized curlew with dark crown and pale crownstripe. Much larger than other curlews with crownstripes except *N. tahitiensis*, from which by rather dark grey-brown tone to plumage, and lack of bright cinnamon on upper tail-coverts. Palaearctic races also differ in showing white on lower back, (more extensive in west). Smaller than plain-crowned curlews except *N. tenuirostris*, but darker than this species, lacking white on secondaries and inner primaries, and with bill broader and deeper at tip. Bill dark brown, becoming pale brown or fleshy at base. Legs bluish-grey.

AGEING

Ad Scapulars and tertials pale brown with indistinct pale buff/whitish bars and spots. Coverts edged buffish when fresh, but for most of year worn and generally lacking any contrasting pattern. Most start moult in wintering areas August/September and complete November/January. Primaries fresh in winter, slightly worn in spring.

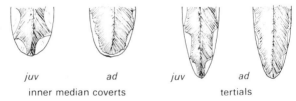

juv   *ad*   *juv*   *ad*
inner median coverts   tertials

Juv Scapulars and tertials with clear buff spotting. Coverts with buff spots, appearing fresh in autumn.

IW Buff spots retained to November but coverts become increasingly notched due to wear of spots; some *Ad* type gained in winter. Primaries slightly worn in winter, moderately worn by spring. Moult is variable, some starting January/March but most not until May/June.

IS Due to great variation in moult pattern only by moderately worn primaries or advanced state of moult; the two moulting groups above complete June/July and October/early November respectively.

SEXING ♀ averages larger.

GEOGRAPHICAL VARIATION Three races recognised: nominate *phaeopus* (Iceland-W. USSR), *variegatus* (central-E. USSR) and *hudsonicus* (Nearctic). Separated by:

	N.p. phaeopus	*N.p. variegatus*	*N.p. hudsonicus*
lower back	white	whitish	brown
rump	white	mostly brown	brown
underwing/axillaries	white:	brown:	brown:
(ground colour: barring)	narrow brown	narrow white	narrow buff

Measurements of races very similar, but *phaeopus* from Iceland and *hudsonicus* are slightly larger.

BIOMETRICS

N.p. phaeopus

Wing	16 A♂	239-255	(245.9)	:	18 J♂	223-249	(233.2)
	12 A♀	232-265	(253.4)	:	20 J♀	225-257	(240.9)
Bill	16 A♂	76-92	(82.1)	:	19 J♂	54-85	(72.7)
	12 A♀	76-99	(83.7)	:	20 J♀	62-91	(77.8)
Tarsus	16 A♂	53-64	(58.0)	:	18 J♂	54-63	(57.8)
	11 A♀	56-65	(61.1)	:	20 J♀	56-61	(59.1)

N.p. variegatus

Wing	24 A	230-256	(242.6)	:	14 J	214-242	(231.7)
Bill	22 A	73-93	(85.9)	:	14 J	63-84	(74.1)
Tarsus	24 A	55-65	(58.7)	:	13 J	52-63	(57.4)

N.p. hudsonicus

Wing	19 A	230-258	(246.0)	:	24 J	221-257	(240.7)
Bill	17 A	82-98	(89.8)	:	23 J	66-99	(80.0)
Tarsus	18 A	54-63	(58.6)	:	25 J	53-62	(57.7)

REFERENCES Moult 69, Variation 133, Biometrics, Weight 70.

BRISTLE-THIGHED CURLEW   *Numenius tahitiensis*

NW N (W. Alaska). Long-distance migrant chiefly to Pacific islands.

IDENTIFICATION Medium-sized curlew with dark crown and pale crownstripe. From *N. phaeopus* by brighter plumage with much rich cinnamon, and upper tail coverts rich cinnamon with only sparse brown barring. Never shows white on back or rump. Shafts of some feathers of rear flanks and thighs are much elongated to form long shiny bristles, diagnostic in the hand. Bill rather thick, dark greyish with fleshy base. Legs thick and rather short, bluish-grey.

AGEING Few specimens examined but apparently similar to other *Numenius*.

Ad Median coverts with fairly distinct olive spots and dark central wedge. Primary coverts tend to be narrowly edged whitish-buff. Outer 4/5 primaries dark, but with slightly paler tips to 6-8. Moult apparently October-late winter, so primaries fresh or moulting in winter, fresh in spring.

median coverts

juv   ad

Juv/IW Coverts broadly edged pale buff, and with large pale cinnamon-buff spots. Primary coverts tipped with large white spots. Primaries 1-8 with relatively clear white tips. Primaries wear rapidly so are moderately worn in winter, very worn by spring.

SEXING and BIOMETRICS   Not enough information available. Ranges (n = 7) : wing 225-260, bill 72-92, tarsus 51-60.

REFERENCES   Moult 69, Weight 70.

SLENDER-BILLED CURLEW   *Numenius tenuirostris*

MC P. Medium-distance migrant (SW to Mediterranean region).

IDENTIFICATION   Medium-sized curlew, lacking crownstripe and dark cap, with plumage distinctively pale. Lower back and rump white, upper tail coverts white sparsely barred and streaked brown. Greater coverts, secondaries and inner primaries boldly spotted with white; underwing and axillaries almost pure white. Ground colour to underparts white; bold heart-shaped brown spots on flanks diagnostic when present. Smaller than *N. arquata,* and with finer bill. Much paler than *N. phaeopus,* lacking crownstripe, and with bill more tapering and much finer at tip. Bill dark brown, fleshy underneath at base. Legs dark bluish-grey.

AGEING

Ad   Clear heart-shaped flank spots in *SP,* but in *WP* with more streaks on underparts and flank spots less distinct. Primaries 1-6 (rarely 7) tipped white. Moult completed by early winter, so primaries are fresh in winter, slightly worn in spring, and moderately worn in autumn.

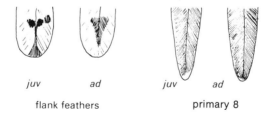

juv   ad   juv   ad

flank feathers   primary 8

Juv   Brown flank streaks; no heart-shaped spots. Primaries 1-8 (sometimes 9) tipped white.

IW   White primary tips wear away rapidly to be moderately worn by midwinter, with point at tip of shaft of primary 8. Some heart-shaped spots attained by late winter.

IS   Only by very worn primaries.

Plate 9 LONG-BILLED DOWITCHER: JUVENILE. *The dark feathers of mantle, scapulars and tertials with very narrow, slightly scalloped edging are species-as well as age-diagnostic characters. Note the virtual absence of internal pale markings on these feathers, and especially the dark tertials with only a very narrow fringe and tip.*

UPLAND SANDPIPER: JUVENILE. *Characteristic appearance of slightly downcurved bill, large eye, small head and long tail. Age by dark subterminal spot inside pale buff fringes on most coverts, and blackish scapulars and tertials with narrow whitish fringes.*

Plate 10 SPOTTED REDSHANK: JUVENILE/FIRST WINTER. *Note juvenile coverts and tertials with striking pale spots and fringes, while the juvenile mantle feathers are being replaced by adult type uniform grey ones with very fine whitish margin. Only a trace remains of distinctive dark flank bars of juvenile.*

REDSHANK: JUVENILE. *Ageing by large buffish spots on tips of coverts and along tertials.*

Plate 11 GREENSHANK: JUVENILE. *Note lack of SP adults' spotted breast, and especially the covert pattern with a pale fringe interrupted centrally by a fairly wide dark wedge.*

TURNSTONE: JUVENILE. *Ageing by dark and relatively small scapulars and coverts with even narrow pale (buff) fringes.*

Plate 12 LESSER YELLOWLEGS: FIRST WINTER. *Note fading buff spots on edges of coverts, also tertials with pale wedges wearing and beginning to give notched appearance.*

WOOD SANDPIPER: JUVENILE. *Ageing character is bold buff spots on coverts, scapulars and tertials. Bolder spotting and more distinct supercilium than juvenile Green Sandpiper (see Plate 13).*

Plate 13 GREEN SANDPIPER: ADULT, AUTUMN. *Ageing by relatively few indistinct whitish spots on coverts and tertials, and much more heavily marked breast.*

GREEN SANDPIPER: JUVENILE. *From adult by distinct small (buff-brown) spots on mantle, coverts and tertials.*

Plate 14 COMMON SANDPIPER: ADULT, AUTUMN. *Traces of SP remain on the scapulars and the worn, sparsely-barred coverts are characteristic of adult.*

SPOTTED SANDPIPER: JUVENILE. *The strongly-barred coverts and sub-terminal dark fringes to mantle and scapulars identify this bird as a juvenile. The very clear and contrasting area of strongly-barred coverts is a good feature of Spotted Sandpiper in this plumage. Note also the proportionately shorter tail.*

Plate 15 WILSON'S PHALAROPE: FIRST WINTER. *Note distinctive shape and whitish colour and for ageing a mixture of adult type pale grey coverts and a few dark juvenile ones with distinct pale buff fringes.*

RED-NECKED PHALAROPE: ADULT FEMALE SUMMER. *The distinct pattern on head and neck is useful for sexing and note the very fine bill.*

Plate 16 GREY PHALAROPE: ADULT, WINTER. *Note for ageing the uniform pale grey coverts and mantle with only very narrow white edges. Also compare shortish stout bill with Red-necked.*

GREY PHALAROPE: JUVENILE. *The bill is short and broad in comparison with Red-necked Phalarope and also dark mantle has pale edgings but no sign of pale lines on scapulars. Also some adult type winter feathers are coming in on back.*

SEXING ♀ averages larger, especially in bill length.

BIOMETRICS Small samples, ages combined.

Wing	7FGơ	243-259	(252.9)	: 6FG♀	248-271	(261.3)
Bill	7FGơ	69-76	(72.7)	: 6FG♀	76-95	(87.6)
Tarsus	7FGơ	61-64	(62.6)	: 6FG♀	62-67	(64.3)

CURLEW   *Numenius arquata*

M P. Short- medium- or long-distance migrant.

IDENTIFICATION Large curlew lacking cap and crownstripe; only large curlew with white lower back and rump. Greater coverts, secondaries and inner primaries boldly spotted white or brownish-white. Underwing and axillaries almost pure white, or slightly marked brown in *N.a. arquata*. Usually browner than *N. tenuirostris* particularly on breast *(N.a. orientalis* especially can be as pale), but always larger, with bill thicker and less tapering and almost always longer. Larger and paler than *N. phaeopus* and lacking crownstripe. Bill dark brown, fleshy underneath at base. Legs bluish-grey.

AGEING

Ad General buff-brown colour; coverts have indistinct grey-brown centres and paler edges, but they wear quite rapidly. Scapulars brownish with indistinct grey-brown barring; in fresh *SP* gain brighter *Juv* type scapulars but these are fresh rather than worn as in *Juv*. Moult end July-November, slightly later in eastern birds; so primaries are fresh in winter, slightly worn in spring. Primaries usually noticeably rounded.

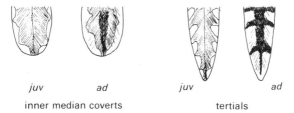

juv   ad   juv   ad

inner median coverts   tertials

Juv Upperparts with very extensive buff edges. Coverts have distinct brown central mark and bright buff edges. Scapulars brown, heavily notched buff.

IW Coverts fade rapidly, and *IW* are best distinguished by scapulars. The buff spots wear away fairly quickly; retained feathers are heavily notched by early winter, contrasting markedly with fresh *Ad* type scapulars moulted in. Some gain all *Ad* type scapulars by February/March, but by then primary wear is helpful. Primaries slight worn in winter, moderately worn by spring. Primaries tend to be pointed.

IS Primaries moderately worn. Usually start to moult May, probably completing August.

SEXING ♀ averages larger. Most birds can be sexed on a combination of two mensural characters (below); most of the remainder will be correctly sexed on a combination of three characters.

	N.a. arquata		*N.a. orientalis*	
	A ♂ A♀	J ♂ J♀	A ♂ A♀	J ♂ J♀
Wing	< 300 >	< 300 >	< 305 >	< 300 >
Bill	< 140 >	< 130 >	< 145 >	< 150 >
Tarsus	< 80 >	< 80 >	< 85 >	< 85 >

GEOGRAPHICAL VARIATION Two races recognized: *arquata* (Europe), and *orientalis* (Urals eastwards). Nominate *arquata* has greyer tinge in *SP*, and axillaries white clearly marked brown. *Orientalis* is buffer in *SP*, generally paler, and with axillaries white sometimes with small brown subterminal mark; it is also slightly larger especially in bill and tarsus. These differences are slight and only clear in a series of birds as there is considerable variation.

BIOMETRICS

N.a. arquata

Wing	22 A♂	273-303	(290.9)	:	22 J♂	270-309	(284.6)
	16 A♀	300-324	(309.1)	:	18 J♀	290-325	(302.8)
Bill	23 A♂	95-141	(115.5)	:	21 J♂	83-135	(111.6)
	15 A♀	138-185	(152.9)	:	18 J♀	107-167	(141.1)
Tarsus	23 A♂	67-84	(74.7)	:	22 J♂	69-85	(75.5)
	16 A♀	72-92	(83.1)	:	19 J♀	74-87	(82.0)

N.a. orientalis

Wing	11 A♂	284-305	(293.4)	:	19 J♂	269-298	(286.9)
	15 A♀	297-322	(309.5)	:	17 J♀	289-315	(303.9)
Bill	14 A♂	123-146	(134.5)	:	18 J♂	114-150	(136.1)
	16 A♀	138-184	(165.9)	:	19 J♀	152-188	(166.7)
Tarsus	14 A♂	78-85	(81.9)	:	18 J♂	74-86	(81.2)
	17 A♀	79-91	(86.4)	:	19 J♀	85-90	(87.3)

REFERENCES Moult 6, 126, Weight 92.

LONG-BILLED CURLEW *Numenius americanus*

MW N. Short- or medium-distance migrant.

IDENTIFICATION Large curlew with streaked crown (no crownstripe), dark lower back and rump, and very distinctive colours. Bright cinnamon secondaries and inner primaries, barred brown. Underwing and axillaries rich cinnamon with sparse brown bars; underparts washed cinnamon, particularly rich in *SP*. *N. madagascariensis* is similar but lacks cinnamon. *Limosa fedoa* has similar colours but is smaller with bill straight or slightly upturned, and *N. borealis* is much smaller with a crownstripe. Bill dusky, fleshy underneath at base, averaging longer than *N. arquata*. Legs bluish-grey.

AGEING

Ad Coverts as *Juv* but slightly browner. Tertials and scapulars with narrow brown central marks and dull grey-buff pale areas. Pale cinnamon tips to primaries 1-7 (rarely 8). Moult August-October, so primaries fresh in winter, slightly worn in spring, and by early autumn moderately worn.

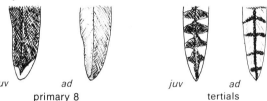

juv   *ad*   *juv*   *ad*
primary 8   tertials

Juv Coverts slightly buffer than *Ad*. Tertials and scapulars with broad brown central marks and clear cinnamon-buff notches. Primaries pointed and with noticeably pale tips to 1-8 (often 9).

IW Primary tips wear rapidly, so by midwinter are moderately worn with distinct shaft point on primary 8. *Juv* tertials and scapulars may be retained.

IS Only by very worn primaries.

SEXING ♀ averages larger, especially in bill length.

GEOGRAPHICAL VARIATION Two races recognized: *americanus* (central USA) and *parvus* (S. Canada, N. USA). Very similar, but *americanus* reported to have much larger bill.

BIOMETRICS races combined.

Wing	7 A♂	258-287	(271.0) : 4 J♂	266-284	(276.2)
	12 A♀	265-295	(281.7) : 5 J♀	257-296	(277.4)
Bill	7 A♂	114-173	(138.6) : 4 J♂	113-147	(127.7)
	12 A♀	144-202	(170.2) : 4 J♀	154-209	(179.5)
Tarsus	8 A♂	72-83	(78.0) : 4 J♂	74-80	(76.5)
	12 A♀	78-92	(83.4) : 5 J♀	74-86	(79.6)

EASTERN CURLEW   *Numenius madagascariensis*

ME P. Medium- to long-distance migrant.

IDENTIFICATION Largest curlew, with plumage similar to *N. arquata* except for dark lower back and rump, and axillaries white heavily barred brown. Also rather darker, especially on belly and flanks, and often with massively long bill. Secondaries and inner primaries spotted with brownish-white. Resembles *N. americanus* but lacks extensive cinnamon and is more heavily marked on underparts and underwing. Bill dark brown becoming fleshy underneath at base, legs bluish-grey.

AGEING

Ad Mantle and scapulars brown, with only a trace of cinnamon. Coverts brown with paler edges, becoming whitish with worn edges in winter. Outer primary covert more or less uniform dark brown. Primaries 1-6 tipped white. Moult late autumn-January/February, so primaries are fresh in winter and spring.

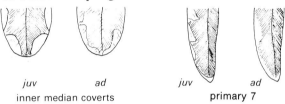

juv   ad   juv   ad

inner median coverts   primary 7

Juv/IW Upperparts and especially coverts with extensive buffish-white edgings. Outer primary covert tends to be tipped white. Primaries 1-8 tipped white. Underparts also tend to have finer streaking than *Ad*. Primaries slightly worn in early winter, moderately worn by late winter/spring.

IS Occasionally by primary covert but best by very worn primaries.

SEXING Very few sexed birds examined but ♀ on average with larger bill (4 A♂ 128-170, x̄ 155 : 4 A♀ 154-201, x̄ 184). Sexes fairly similar in wing and tarsus.

BIOMETRICS sexes combined.

Wing	23 A	290-333	(316.9) :	22 J	281-314	(294.8)
Bill	23 A	128-201	(175.1) :	22 J	105-186	(145.9)
Tarsus	23 A	81-95	(88.6) :	22 J	77-92	(85.3)

UPLAND SANDPIPER   *Bartramia longicauda*

NW, MC and ME N. Long-distance migrant.

IDENTIFICATION Short-billed and long-tailed wader like a largish *Tringa,* but with plumage recalling tiny *Numenius.* Crown dark brown with pale buffish crownstripe; mantle and coverts brown, barred dark brown and tipped buffish. Remiges mainly dark with narrow whitish trailing edge to secondaries. Lower back blackish, rump and upper tail-coverts blackish with narrow white sides. Longish well-rounded tail, with outer feathers 3-6 pale orange-brown basally and tipped white, and all feathers barred dark brown. Breast washed buffish; upper breast streaked brown, lower breast and flanks more barred. Underwing and axillaries whitish, heavily barred brown. Bill short and thin, dark brown with paler base. Legs yellowish. *See Plate 9.*

AGEING

Ad Scapulars rich pale brown with distinct dark brown bars, edged creamy-buff at first. Coverts and tertials dark olive-buff with brown bars. Moult October-January, so primaries are fresh in spring and slightly worn in autumn.

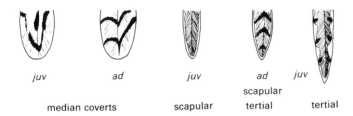

juv   ad   juv   ad   juv

scapular

median coverts   scapular   tertial   tertial

Juv/IW Scapulars dark blackish-brown, sometimes with trace of darker brown markings, and thin pale buff edges, usually wearing away by October although sometimes retained to spring (when very worn). Tertials dark brown with pale buff edges and notches. Coverts pale brown fringed pale buff and with brown crescentic subterminal spot, giving a scaly appearance; the edges wear off, sometimes remaining clear on inner medians until spring, but many coverts are replaced in winter. Primaries are slightly worn in winter, moderately worn in spring.

IS Identified by moderately worn brownish primaries. Moult starts usually early in August (often suspending).

SEXING ♀ averages larger.

BIOMETRICS

Wing	18 A♂	163-180	(169.8) :	10 J♂	163-176	(167.4)
	7 A♀	164-191	(174.4) :	7 J♀	167-179	(170.0)
Bill	17 A♂	26-31	(29.1) :	12 J♂	27-32	(29.6)
	7 A♀	29-35	(31.1) :	8 J♀	26-32	(30.4)
Tarsus	18 A♂	46-52	(48.8) :	10 J♂	45-50	(48.3)
	7 A♀	45-50	(47.9) :	7 J♀	48-50	(48.7)

SPOTTED REDSHANK   *Tringa erythropus*

N P. Medium- to long-distance migrant.

IDENTIFICATION Medium-sized to large *Tringa*. White rump and lower back but upper tail coverts heavily barred. Secondaries and inner primaries spotted or notched white, giving a broad but poorly-contrasting pale trailing edge to wing. Sooty-black head and underparts in *SP*, and heavy brownish-grey barring and suffusion beneath in juveniles are diagnostic. Rather plain pale grey above and whitish below in *WP*. Bill rather thin and long, blackish becoming dull red towards base. Legs orange-red, or dark reddish-brown in *SP*. Always from *T. totanus* by slightly larger size, longer bill and legs, and darker secondaries. *See Plate 10.*

AGEING Can be difficult after November.

Ad SP Upperparts black, at first with whitish tips; scapulars and mantle notched white. Underparts black, with variable amount of whitish on belly.

WP Upperparts grey. Coverts and scapulars grey-brown with large white fringes and subterminal brown bars, but beware inner medians with small pale spots (resembling *Juv* spotting but smaller and whiter). Moult late July-September, so primaries are fresh in winter, slightly worn in spring, moderately worn by summer. Note that wear on primaries and other feathers depends on the wintering areas; those wintering in temperate zones should be ageable but many in the tropics are very difficult.

inner median coverts

juv   ad

Juv Upperparts darkish brown, spotted white. Coverts, especially outer medians, with distinct large spots at sides, and at tip a pair of lateral spots and a large dark central area. Underparts whitish, heavily washed and barred brownish-grey.

IW Resembles *Ad WP*. Most spotting on median coverts is lost by winter; underpart barring lost by late October/mid November. Primaries slightly worn in winter, moderately worn by spring. Tail feathers narrow with pointed tips.

IS Only by very worn primaries and central tail feathers. Usually have very worn median and lesser coverts. Many attain full *SP* and moult as *Ad*.

SEXING ♀ averages larger. In *SP* ♂ has mainly blackish central under tail coverts and completely black distal half of crown feathers; ♀ has mainly white central under tail coverts and pale edges to blackish crown feathers.

BIOMETRICS Apparently no geographical variation.

Wing	19 A♂	158-173	(167.0)	:	13 J♂	159-173	(166.1)
	16 A♀	162-178	(170.1)	:	20 J♀	166-180	(170.6)
Bill	17 A♂	54-62	(57.4)	:	10 J♂	53-61	(56.9)
	17 A♀	55-62	(58.9)	:	18 J♀	52-62	(59.0)
Tarsus	20 A♂	52-61	(58.6)	:	13 J♂	52-62	(56.6)
	18 A♀	54-60	(56.9)	:	20 J♀	54-61	(57.2)

REDSHANK   *Tringa totanus*

M and S P. Short- medium- or long-distance migrant.

IDENTICATION   Medium-sized to large *Tringa* with diagnostic white
secondaries. Also lower back and rump white, and white at tips of inner
primaries. Bill straight, reddish at base but distal half blackish. Legs orange-
red, very bright in *SP*. Wing and tail pattern preclude confusion with
Philomachus pugnax. Rather smaller than *T. erythropus* and with shorter bill
and legs. *Xenus cinereus* has secondaries extensively white, but legs are yellow,
back is dark, and upcurved bill is unmistakeable. *See Plate 10.*

AGEING

Ad SP   Upperparts brown and underparts white with variable amount of dark
     brown barring and spotting, depending on race. Coverts grey-brown
     edged paler on outers, white on inners.

WP   Upperparts grey-brown, coverts as *SP* (inners fringed white). Tertials
     grey-brown either plain or with dark sepia bars; rounded at tip.
     Underparts white, with breast washed grey and finely streaked brown.
     Moult July-October in W. Palaearctic, July-February in E. Palaearctic;
     so primaries are fresh in winter, and slightly worn in spring (least worn
     in spring in E. Palaearctic birds).

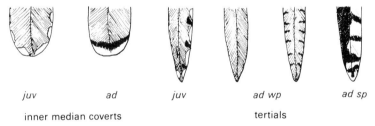

| juv | ad | juv | ad wp | ad sp |
| inner median coverts | | | tertials | |

Juv   Upperparts and coverts warm brown with extensive buff fringes.
     Tertials lanceolate, brown with buff spots. Breast buff-brown, slightly
     streaked. Tail feathers pointed, with reddish suffusion at tip. Bill dull
     reddish.

IW   As *Ad WP* but buff-tipped inner medians (with dark central mark
     interrupting the fringe) retained to spring. Some brown lanceolate
     tertials usually retained through winter, and when worn these have
     characteristic notched appearance. Tail feathers pointed and with
     reddish suffusion usually distinct into the winter. Primaries slightly
     worn in winter, fairly worn in spring; great contrast with adults in E, less
     in W Palaearctic.

IS   Sometimes inner medians are retained but moderately worn primaries
     are the best guide. Most attain *SP*. Primary moult may start from April,
     especially in SE Asia.

SEXING ♀ averages larger, but there is great overlap of sexes and much geographical variation.

GEOGRAPHICAL VARIATION A variable species with six races recognised and clinal variations between them. Variation is known in wing, bill, tarsus and tail length, and tarsus width. There are also significant variations in the amount of *SP* attained and the basic colour (grey, brown, light or dark cinnamon, erythristic). For the full summary of the data see Hale (1971). This review recognises only two races in Europe: *robusta* (Iceland) and nominate *totanus* (Spain, Scandinavia); the rest of the Redshank in the British Isles, N. France, Belgium, Netherlands, West Germany and Denmark form a hybrid zone and *'britannica'* is no longer considered separable. *Robusta* differs from other European birds in larger wing, smaller bill, and in partial *SP* on back and breast having grey or cinnamon suffusion.

Biometric averages and summer plumage tendencies of W. European Redshank
(Hale 1971)

		Iceland	Britain	N. Scand	S. Scand	W. Europe	SW Europe
extent of *SP* on back and scaps		½	¼	full	¾	⅔	⅔
breast suffusion		yes	yes	no	no	slight	no
breast spotting		medium	light	heavy	heavy	medium	heavy
wing	♀	170	163	160	162	162	160
	♂	167	160	157	157	160	158
bill	♀	41.5	42.5	41	41.5	43	44
	♂	39	42	39.5	40.5	42	43

BIOMETRICS (of breeding birds, from Hale 1971)

♂	wing		bill		tarsus
robusta: Iceland	160-176 (167.2)	:	37.0-42.5 (39.0)	:	44.0-48.2 (47.4)
(britannica)	149-168 (159.2)	:	37.0-44.5 (41.3)	:	44.0-51.0 (47.4)
totanus: Spain, Scandinavia	150-165 (157.5)	:	34.0-44.0 (41.2)	:	41.0-54.0 (46.8)
eurhinus: SW China	158-169 (163.2)	:	41.5-49.0 (45.4)	:	45.5-53.5 (49.7)
ussuriensis: NC Asia	152-170 (160.5)	:	38.0-46.6 (42.7)	:	45.2-54.9 (50.7)
craggii: NW China	153-164 (158.5)	:	44.5 (44.5)	:	47.0-51.0 (49.0)
terrignotae: E. China	154-160 (157.0)	:	41.5-46.0 (42.9)	:	41.5-51.5 (48.3)
♀					
robusta	163-175 (170.4)	:	38.0-44.5 (41.5)	:	46.0-52.0 (48.6)
(britannica)	156-172 (162.5)	:	40.0-44.0 (42.0)	:	45.0-51.0 (47.9)
totanus	154-174 (161.0)	:	38.5-46.0 (42.4)	:	43.5-54.5 (48.4)
eurhinus	157-172 (164.3)	:	41.5-50.0 (46.1)	:	44.0-54.0 (49.4)
ussuriensis	156-167 (160.6)	:	40.0-48.0 (41.8)	:	46.8-55.0 (48.7)
craggii	156-162 (159.4)	:	43.5-45.0 (44.7)	:	47.0-50.0 (48.2)
terrignotae	157-160 (158.3)	:	43.5-46.0 (45.0)	:	46.5-52.5 (49.3)

REFERENCES Moult 6, 120, Sex 46, Variation 46, 47, Biometrics 5, 27, 36, 45, 46, 47, 117, Weight 92, 117, 127.

MARSH SANDPIPER   *Tringa stagnatilis*

MC and ME P. Medium- or long-distance migrant.

IDENTIFICATION Smallish *Tringa* with proportionately long legs. White rump and lower back; tail whitish irregularly marked brown. Wing plain, but with very narrow whitish tips to fresh greater coverts and secondaries. Almost straight bill, very fine and tapering to a very sharp tip, blackish tinged greenish at base. Rather spindly olive-green legs. Recalls *T. nebularia* and *T. guttifer*, but these are much larger with bills thickish and slightly upturned.

AGEING

Ad SP Mantle mottled grey/dark brown. Coverts and scapulars grey-brown barred brown. Underparts white, with breast spotted and flanks barred brown.

WP Upperparts grey-brown. Coverts greyish with complete narrow white fringe; feathers rounder and less worn than in *IW*. Most moult late August to end October before reaching the wintering area but some, probably the small percentage that suspend moult, do not complete until early winter (and a few in the south of range not until February). Therefore wide variation in amount of wear, but typically fresh in midwinter, wearing rapidly towards summer when a few almost as worn as *IS*.

juv   iw   ad

inner median coverts

Juv Mantle, coverts and scapulars dark brown, heavily spotted or edged buff. Underparts white.

IW As *Ad WP* but some brown on back retained to October/November. Some inner medians are retained into the winter, when are recognisable by brownish colour with the central dark area breaking the faded and very worn buff edges, and by much more pointed tip. Primaries fresh in autumn, slightly worn during winter. Some (<25%) replace outer 2-4 primaries from January-May. In spring primaries either all moderately worn or showing contrast between fresh outers and worn inners.

IS By primary wear only, either very worn or with contrast between outers and inners. Some attain *SP*. Often start moult June-July.

SEXING ♀ averages larger.

141

BIOMETRICS

Wing	28Ao'	134-145	(139.8)	:	11Jo'	128-141	(135.8)
	24A♀	135-148	(141.7)	:	12J♀	138-145	(141.2)
Bill	22Ao'	38-42	(39.6)	:	11Jo'	38-45	(40.4)
	20A♀	36-45	(40.8)	:	12J♀	38-44	(41.0)
Tarsus	29Ao'	47-56	(51.7)	:	12Jo'	47-57	(51.5)
	23A♀	48-57	(51.9)	:	14J♀	47-55	(51.0)

REFERENCES Moult 112, 153, Weight 113.

GREENSHANK   *Tringa nebularia*

N and M P. Medium- to long-distance migrant.

IDENTIFICATION Large *Tringa* with stoutish, slightly upturned bill, greyish-green at base, and legs pale olive-green (very rarely yellow). Lower back and rump white; tail pale grey-brown, whiter at sides. No wingbar, but narrow whitish tips to coverts, secondaries and inner primaries especially in juveniles. Larger and with much stouter bill than *T. stagnatilis*. Very similar to *T. guttifer* but has longer legs, axillaries and underwing white with sparse brown flecking and barring, and spotting on underparts in *SP* often less extensive. *See Plate 11.*

AGEING

Ad SP Upperparts brownish-grey/dark brown. Coverts brownish-grey, with inners fringed white. Underparts white; upper breast streaked and spotted blackish-brown.

WP Upperparts greyish, coverts grey with inners fringed white. Central tail feather whitish, strongly barred brown. Underparts white; very fine streaking on breast. Moult July-November (later in southern part of range), so primaries are fresh in winter, slightly worn by spring.

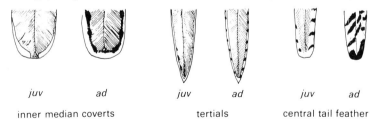

juv	ad	juv	ad	juv	ad
inner median coverts		tertials		central tail feather	

Juv Upperparts dark brown, broadly edged buff-brown. Coverts grey-brown with broad buff fringes interrupted centrally by brown bar. Central tail feather has greyish central area, fringed whitish, with small brown bars. Underparts white; breast sparsely streaked and mottled, lower breast and flanks with many narrow brown crescentic bars.

IW   As *Ad WP* but some *Juv* inner medians often retained to spring, but by then fringes are worn away leaving brownish feathers. Primaries slightly worn by midwinter. In E. Africa a few and S. Africa many birds moult outer primaries February-May. So in spring primaries either moderately worn or showing contrast between old inners and fresh outers.

IS   Primaries either very worn or with contrast in wear. Sometimes central tail feathers are not replaced and these become very worn. Some in the north may attain *SP*. Many remain south of breeding areas in *WP* and may start moult earlier than adults.

SEXING   ♀ usually slightly larger.

GEOGRAPHICAL VARIATION   (per P. Rose *in litt.*) No races described but largest populations breed in central USSR, with decrease in size to E. and W.

BIOMETRICS   Birds on breeding grounds (per P. Rose):

		Scandinavia			*Central USSR*			*E. USSR*		
		mean	SD	n :	mean	SD	n :	mean	SD	n
Wing	♂	189.5	3.74	10 :	191.2	4.94	11 :	187.6	3.97	8
	♀	189.7	3.55	12 :	191.3	1.65	5 :	184.9	5.22	4
Bill	♂	53.9	2.07	10 :	54.2	1.82	11 :	53.7	1.69	8
	♀	55.8	2.55	11 :	56.9	2.41	5 :	52.6	1.03	4
Tarsus	♂	60.7	2.74	9 :	59.9	2.05	11 :	60.1	3.12	8
	♀	60.4	1.99	11 :	62.2	2.85	5 :	58.5	0.58	4
Tail	♂	79.0	3.31	9 :	80.4	2.76	10 :	76.7	2.39	8
	♀	78.2	2.94	11 :	80.2	1.89	5 :	79.9	4.03	4

For 39 *Juv* in W. Europe, wing 177-195 (186.4).

REFERENCES   General 98, Moult 6, 112, 120, 153, Biometrics, Weight 117.

ARMSTRONG'S SANDPIPER   *Tringa guttifer*

ME P (Sakhalin). Short- to medium-distance migrant.

IDENTIFICATION   Largish *Tringa* with white lower back and rump and no wingbar, very similar to *T. nebularia* but with shorter legs and with underwing and axillaries pure white. Spotted underparts in *SP* are similar to *T. nebularia* but sometimes extending well onto flanks and belly, and neck also is spotted (tends to be more streaked in *T. nebularia*). Bill stoutish and upturned as *T. nebularia*, but basal half is more yellowish. Legs short, pale green but sometimes yellowish.

AGEING

Ad SP Upperparts blackish-brown with white spots, which abrade rapidly. Underparts white with blackish-brown spots on breast, and some also on neck and flanks.

WP Upperparts grey; coverts grey edged white, tertials grey. Moult completed by November, so primaries are fresh in winter.

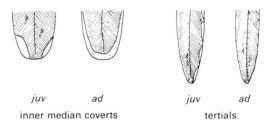

juv   ad   juv   ad
inner median coverts   tertials

Juv Upperparts brown with extensive buff streaks and spots. Coverts brownish narrowly edged pale whitish-buff. Tertials brownish, spotted buff. Underparts white, with breast and neck washed brown.

IW As *Ad WP* but with retained brownish inner medians and tertials, becoming worn. Primaries slightly worn by early winter.

IS Moderately worn primaries. Some attain *SP*.

SEXING No characters found, but few examined and no *Ad ♂*.

BIOMETRICS (no A ♂ examined)

Wing	3 A♀ 177-182	(180.0) :	6 J♀ 169-183	(177.0)
			5 J♂ 174-181	(177.8)
Bill	3 A♀˙ 53-56	(54.0) :	6 J♀ 48-58	(53.7)
			5 J♂ 49-57	(54.0)
Tarsus	3 A♀ 44-45	(44.3) :	6 J♀ 43-48	(44.8)
			5 J♂ 42-47	(44.8)

GREATER YELLOWLEGS   *Tringa melanoleuca*

N N. Medium- to long-distance migrant.

IDENTIFICATION Largest *Tringa*, with structure resembling *T. nebularia* but has bright yellow legs and white on rump but not extending up lower back. No wingbar, but coverts, secondaries and inner primaries with more distinct whitish spotting than in *T. nebularia*. Bill stout, slightly upturned, very dark with greenish tinge at base. Very similar in plumage pattern and soft part colour to *T. flavipes*, which however is distinctly smaller and more delicate with a much thinner bill.

144

AGEING

Ad SP Upperparts a mixture of light and dark brown feathers with whitish spots. Coverts light brown with ill-defined pale whitish tips and dark brown lateral subterminal spots. Underparts white with distinct dark bars on breast and flanks.

WP Upperparts grey-brown, coverts as *SP*. Underparts white, with breast streaked brown. Moult August-January, so primaries are fresh in winter, slightly worn by summer.

  inner median coverts

juv   *ad*

Juv Upperparts brown with buff spots. On the coverts spots form series along the edges of feathers leaving a broad dark central bar at tip.

IW As *Ad WP* but slightly browner. Spots fade and wear quickly but pattern remains clear; some inner medians are retained to spring. Primaries slightly worn in winter, moderately worn by spring.

IS Only by moderately worn primaries. Many attain partial and some full *SP*.

SEXING Very small differences in size.

BIOMETRICS and GEOGRAPHICAL VARIATION (per P. Rose) — breeding birds.

		Alaska/W. Canada			*Alberta/Manitoba*			*Ontario/Quebec*		
		mean	SD	n :	mean	SD	n :	mean	SD	n
Wing	A♂	190.7	6.17	16 :	195.1	3.61	6 :	189.9	7.27	15
	A♀	190.7	3.98	9 :	199.4	4.46	4 :	193.2	10.14	5
Bill	A♂	55.3	1.98	16 :	53.6	3.02	6 :	54.6	2.04	16
	A♀	54.6	1.85	9 :	54.0	0.91	4 :	53.6	2.69	4
Tarsus	A♂	61.6	2.52	16 :	63.0	2.76	6 :	63.0	2.25	16
	A♀	60.6	3.75	9 :	66.1	3.17	4 :	63.1	0.82	5

Juveniles measured by us were as follows:—

Wing	9 J♂	186-200	(193.4) :	20 J♀	185-205	(196.5)
Bill	9 J♂	50-60	(55.9) :	20 J♀	51-61	(56.1)
Tarsus	9 J♂	59-66	(62.3) :	21 J♀	56-70	(62.4)

REFERENCES Age 14, Weight 86.

LESSER YELLOWLEGS   *Tringa flavipes*

N N. Medium- to long-distance migrant.

IDENTIFICATION   Medium-sized *Tringa* with longish bright yellow legs and white rump patch not extending up back. Similar in plumage and soft part colour to *T. melanoleuca*, but smaller and with a much finer blackish bill which is usually straight (but sometimes drooped at tip). Also resembles *T. glareola* but is larger and longer-legged, with legs much brighter and supercilium less distinct. *See Plate 12.*

AGEING   For primary wear, moult and covert details see table below.

Ad SP   Back black/white with extensive grey-white tips; wears rapidly to blackish. Underparts white, with breast lightly streaked and spotted brown.

WP   Tertials grey-brown, barred dark brown. Moult is variable probably depending on latitude, starting September-November and completing January-March.

Juv   Back and tertials brown with extensive buff spotting. Breast indistinctly streaked, with greyish wash.

IW   Scapulars and tertials brown, extensively notched. Some may moult outer primaries.

IS   Primaries very worn (or with contrast of new outers and old inners).

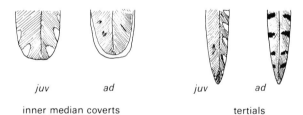

juv   ad   juv   ad

inner median coverts   tertials

		autumn	winter	spring	summer
Primary wear	A	slight	moderate/fresh	fresh	slight
	J	fresh	slight	moderate	very
Moult	A	none	Sept.-Mar.	none	none
	J	none	none	outers in some	none/contrast
Median coverts	A	brown-grey with white edge dark sub-lateral spots; wearing		as autumn	
	J	brown/buff spots	brown worn	replaced by *Ad.* type	

146

GEOGRAPHICAL VARIATION (per P. Rose). There is a slight trend towards central breeding birds having larger wings but differences are small. The averages are:—

breeding	♂Alaska	BC/ Yukon	Alb./ Sask.	Man./ Ont.	♀ Alaska	BC/ Yukon	Alb./ Sask.	Man./ Ont.
Wing	158.7	159.0	160.4	157.6	161.9	162.5	161.7	160.5
Bill	35.6	35.9	35.7	35.9	35.1	36.0	36.0	36.3
Tarsus	52.1	50.9	51.9	51.9	51.9	51.6	52.6	52.2

BIOMETRICS (covering whole range)

Wing	10 A♂	149-168	(160.5) :	8 J♂	152-163		(156.5)
	17 A♀	155-169	(162.1) :	16 J♀	153-166		(161.2)
Bill	37 A	33-40	(36.6) :	31 J	33-40		(36.1)
Tarsus	36 A	47-58	(52.3) :	33 J	46-56		(51.2)

REFERENCES Age 14, Weight 86.

SOLITARY SANDPIPER   *Tringa solitaria*

N N. Medium- to long-distance migrant.

IDENTIFICATION Smallish, short-legged *Tringa* with dark greenish-brown upperparts and dark centre to rump and tail. Sides of rump and tail white heavily barred blackish-brown. No wingbar; underwing and axillaries white, heavily barred blackish-brown. Bill shortish, almost straight, dark greenish-brown. Legs olive-green (rarely yellowish). Plumage very similar to *T. ochropus* which however is larger with a darker underwing and a pure white rump. Larger and darker than *Actitis hypoleucos* and *A. macularia*, and lacking wingbar.

AGEING

Ad Median coverts grey-brown with whitish fringes in autumn; these wear off during winter but white- and buff-spotted outer medians are gained during the spring moult. Moult and wear helpful:

	autumn	*winter*	*spring*	*summer*
Ad	slight wear	moulting	fresh	fairly fresh
Juv/IW	fresh	slight wear	mod. wear	very worn

inner median coverts

juv   ad

Juv Median coverts brown with lateral buff spots. Upper breast with reddish-brown tinge.

IW Buff spots on coverts wear rapidly and are only visible on inner medians after early winter.

IS Primary wear is useful, see above.

SEXING ♀ averages larger, but geographical variation makes this character difficult to use outside breeding season.

GEOGRAPHICAL VARIATION Two races recognized: nominate *solitaria* (E. N. America), with pale buff spots on mantle and coverts, and *cinnamomea* (W. N. America), with brownish-buff spots, slightly larger size and usually white mottling on base of underside of outer primary. Breeding ranges merge.

BIOMETRICS races combined.

Wing	26 A♂	125-141	(131.6) : 19 J♂	126-144	(134.2)
	20 A♀	128-146	(138.4) : 16 J♀	125-146	(137.1)
Bill	47 A	27-32	(29.9) : 38 J	27-32	(29.6)
Tarsus	52 A	29-34	(31.3) : 41 J	29-35	(31.5)

GREEN SANDPIPER *Tringa ochropus*

N and M P. Short- medium- or long-distance migrant.

IDENTIFICATION Smallish, short-legged *Tringa* with dark greenish-brown upperparts and dark wings as *T. solitaria* but with bold white rump and upper tail-coverts. Tail barred blackish-brown but outer feathers almost unmarked white. Underwing blackish-brown with narrow white tips and barring. Bill dark brown, tinged greenish at base; legs darkish olive-green. Larger and darker than *T. glareola* with bolder white rump, darker legs, less clear supercilium, and shafts of all primaries dark. *See Plate 13.*

AGEING

Ad SP Upperparts dark olive-brown; when fresh are indistinctly spotted whitish-buff, but by autumn spots are very small. On scapulars and tertials the distal spots are very small.

WP Upperparts as *SP*, with indistinct buffish spotting. Inner lessers and medians initially with small whitish-buff fringes, but these are worn off by midwinter. Two groups of moulting birds, both starting late July/early August: one group suspends in temperate areas then migrates and completes in the south, usually by November but occasionally into December, while the other group completes moult in the north before migrating. Primaries fresh in winter, with outers looking newest, and slightly worn in spring.

148

Juv   Upperparts including coverts mid olive-brown with many distinct deep buff spots. Tertials and scapulars with large whitish subterminal spots.

IW   Spots abrade rapidly but tertial and scapular spots remain to late September. Coverts fade and abrade but buff spots on inner medians are clear to late winter (easiest to see in temperate areas). Primaries slightly worn in midwinter, with outers looking most worn, and moderately worn in spring.

IS   Only by moderately or very worn primaries.

SEXING   ♀ averages larger.

BIOMETRICS

Wing	23 A♂	137-147	(142.6) : 16 J♂	136-148	(140.6)
	27 A♀	140-155	(146.7) : 17 J♀	136-148	(143.8)
Bill	25 A♂	31-38	(34.3) : 17 J♂	31-36	(33.8)
	29 A♀	31-37	(34.5) : 15 J♀	31-38	(34.7)
Tarsus	26 A♂	32-37	(33.9) : 16 J♂	31-36	(33.7)
	31 A♀	31-36	(33.9) : 17 J♀	32-36	(34.1)

REFERENCES   Moult 73, 112, Weight 73.

WOOD SANDPIPER   *Tringa glareola*

N and M P. Medium- to long-distance migrant.

IDENTIFICATION   Smallish *Tringa* with brownish plumage, white rump patch, and usually fairly distinct supercilium. Bill shortish, dark brown tinged greenish or yellowish-brown at base. Legs yellowish-brown or greenish. Slightly smaller and browner than *T. ochropus,* with underwing and axillaries white with brown barring, longer paler legs, smaller white rump patch, and shaft of outer primary white. Smaller and with shorter duller legs than *T. flavipes. See Plate 12.*

AGEING

Ad SP Upperparts and coverts dark brownish-black, barred and spotted pale brown and white; inner medians brown faintly fringed white. Upper breast streaked and spotted dark brown. Bill blackish-brown, greenish at base. Legs usually olive-green or yellowish-green.

WP   Similar but much less contrasting than *SP.* Coverts brown, fringed white. Breast suffused grey-brown, with poorly defined brownish streaks. Moult quite variable but it appears that Siberian and Scandinavian population have different patterns. Scandinavian birds moult from late July-October; a few complete early but most suspend and complete in tropics up to January. Siberian birds appear to migrate to tropics and then moult from late August-February. In

Africa may suspend irregularly. Generally primaries in winter either all very fresh or showing new inners and old outers; during suspension secondaries show new-old-new pattern. In spring all slightly worn, or with a little contrast between slightly worn inners and fresh outers; this pattern is less contrasting than in *IW* and in *Ad* all secondaries are new.

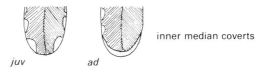

juv   *ad*   inner median coverts

Juv   Upperparts and coverts dark brown, extensively spotted warm buff/brown. Breast heavily suffused grey-brown with pale mottling. Bill dusky-brown or greenish. Legs yellowish- or greenish-brown.

IW   As *Ad WP* but inner medians with buff spots are retained to spring. In winter has characteristic notching on tertials and coverts where buff spots have worn off. Many birds, mostly in the south, renew outer primaries January-May, so showing strong contrast between fresh outers and moderately worn inners. Where contrast is small, check secondaries which in *IW* are moderately worn.

IS   Contrast of old inners and new outers, from similar *Ad* by old secondaries. If there has been no moult, primaries are very worn. Most in the north attain *SP*, fewer in the south.

SEXING   ♀ averages larger.

BIOMETRICS

Wing	23 A♂	120-131	(125.6) : 16 J♂	122-131	(126.5)
	12 A♀	123-131	(127.2) : 21 J♀	124-134	(127.6)
Bill	41 A	27-31	(28.7) : 44 J	25-32	(28.3)
Tarsus	41 A	32-40	(37.0) : 45 J	32-41	(36.7)

REFERENCES   Moult 60, 112, 153, Biometrics, Weight 60.

TEREK SANDPIPER   *Xenus cinereus*

NC and NE P. Long-distance migrant.

IDENTIFICATION   Like a smallish *Tringa* but with short legs and characteristic longish tapering upcurved bill. Grey-brown above, including rump and tail; distinct wing-pattern formed by blackish lesser coverts, grey-brown medians, dark greaters and primaries, and broad white tips to secondaries. Dark lines on mantle in *SP*. Bill blackish becoming orange-yellow at base, legs orange-yellow.

AGEING

Ad SP Upperparts grey-brown, with broad blackish feather centres which are particularly wide on scapulars. Coverts uniform dull grey with dark central line, but some are darkish brown mottled buffish. Tail coverts grey-brown barred sepia. Underparts whitish, with greyish lateral breast patches.

WP Upperparts grey-brown. Coverts grey with narrow white terminal fringe. Moult is variable: most start September-October, suspend, complete December-January but some complete by December without suspending. Primaries fresh in winter, only slightly worn by spring.

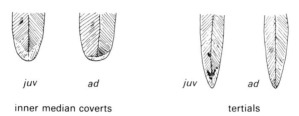

| juv   ad   juv   ad |
| inner median coverts   tertials |

Juv Upperparts brownish-grey with darker shaft streaks, scapulars with larger blackish V-markings. Coverts grey, fringed cinnamon-buff with subterminal brown bar (clearest on tertials). Upper tail coverts and tail tipped brown and cinnamon-buff.

IW As *Ad WP* but some *Juv* tertials and coverts retained to October, and usually to midwinter when are worn (fresh in *Ad*).Primaries slightly worn in late autumn, moderately worn in winter. In the south many moult outer primaries.

IS Primaries either all very worn or showing contrast of old inners and fresh outers. Most attain *SP*.

SEXING ♀ averages larger.

BIOMETRICS

Wing	33 A♂	129-142	(133.5) : 12 J♂	126-134	(128.7)
	21 A♀	131-140	(135.9) : 17 J♀	128-136	(131.6)
Bill	34 A♂	43-52	(46.2) : 11 J♂	39-48	(44.4)
	19 A♀	42-52	(48.0) : 17 J♀	42-51	(47.4)
Tarsus	65 A	26-32	(28.3) : 36 J	26-30	(28.1)

REFERENCES Moult 164, Biometrics 27.

151

COMMON SANDPIPER   *Actitis hypoleucos*

Whole P except extreme N and S. Short- medium- or long-distance migrant. (E).

IDENTIFICATION   Like a small *Tringa* with brown upperparts and rump, and clear white wingbar and trailing edge to secondaries. Bill shortish, dark brown with paler base. Legs pale greenish (rarely yellowish). Smaller and paler than *T. solitaria* and *T. ochropus*, which both lack wingbar. Very similar to *A. macularia* (which see), but in *SP* breast is finely streaked and rest of underparts are white; in *WP* and juvenile is browner, with barring on coverts less pronounced, wingbar and trailing edge broader (usually meeting across inner secondaries), and whitish present on outer webs of outer 2-3 tail feathers. In fresh juveniles tertials are brown with distinct buff and dark brown barring along sides of feathers. Averages larger than *A. macularia*, with proportionately longer tail. *See Plate 14.*

AGEING   A difficult species to age in winter/spring.

Ad SP   Upperparts brown with slight bronze gloss, feathers with dark brown streaking and irregular barring. Coverts fairly uniform brown with darker streaks. Tips of central tail feathers whitish.

WP   During autumn *SP* coverts are lost; new feathers are barred, resembling those of *Juv*, but the bars are dull rufous-buff and brown (duller and less contrasting than *Juv*) and the barred coverts are also usually less extensive. In winter show uniform wear of coverts. Primaries moderately worn in autumn. Moult variable: many start August/ September and suspend, completing up to March, but most E. African birds arrive with primaries all old and moult October-January (March). Birds with suspended or previously suspended moult, or with fresh primaries in winter are *Ad*. In spring either fresh or slightly worn.

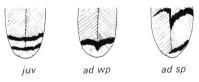

juv   ad wp   ad sp

inner median coverts

Juv   Upperparts brown, with extensive buffish tips and dark subterminal bands. Coverts brown, very heavily barred dark brown and bright rufous-buff. Central tail feathers tipped buffish.

IW   As *Ad WP* but *Juv* inner medians are retained; in winter have contrast of a few very worn inner coverts (almost lace-like in appearance) with replaced fresh *Ad* type ones; by late winter not ageable on coverts. Primaries moderately worn in winter. Moult variable: in tropics and south all moult primaries, and most renew secondaries as well

152

January-April, but a small percentage moult outer primaries only. In spring only ageable if they have strong contrast between old inners and new outers or if old tertials and tail are retained.

IS   Extremely difficult to age. Most gain *SP*.

SEXING   ♀ averages slightly larger.

BIOMETRICS

Wing	15 A♂	107-115	(111.5) : 10 J♂	105-115	(110.4)
	12 A♀	109-116	(112.5) : 17 J♀	107-119	(112.0)
Bill	33 A	22-27	(24.8) : 32 J	22-28	(24.5)
Tarsus	36 A	22-25	(23.6) : 31 J	22-25	(23.6)
Tail	10 A♂	52-58	(55.6) : 10 J♂	51-57	(53.4)
	10 A♀	54-56	(55.5) : 10 J♀	52-57	(54.7)

REFERENCES   Ident. 80B, Moult 10, 112, 153, Biometrics, Weight 10, 117.

SPOTTED SANDPIPER   *Actitis macularia*

Whole N except extreme N and S (has nested MWP). Short- medium- or long-distance migrant.

IDENTIFICATION   Very similar to *A. hypoleucos* (which see), but in *SP* has underparts boldly spotted blackish-brown, and in *WP* and juvenile is rather greyer with coverts more boldly barred. Tertials in juveniles plain brownish-grey with subterminal dark bar and pale tip. Wingbar and trailing edge to secondaries much narrower, usually separated on inner secondaries by about 10 mm. Whitish present on outer webs of only 1-2 outer tail-feathers. Legs and base of bill usually flesh-pink in *SP*, and yellowish in *WP* and juvenile. Tail averages shorter than *A. hypoleucos*. See Plate 14.

juv tertials

A. macularia   A. hypoleucos

AGEING

Ad SP Upperparts and coverts brownish-grey with irregular brown streaking. Underparts white with many blackish spots.

WP   Upperparts as *SP*, but coverts are replaced by barred coverts resembling those of *Juv* although less contrasting. In winter wear is almost uniform on all coverts. Underparts white but some dark spots retained through to September and then regained in March. Primaries moderately worn in autumn. Moult starts in September, most suspending and completing December-March. In winter primaries either very fresh (in a few) or with contrast of new inners and very worn outers. In spring less clear but there is a slight difference between slightly worn inners and fresh outers in those which suspended, otherwise slightly worn.

juv   ad WP   ad SP

inner median coverts

Juv   Mantle plain grey (when very fresh with thin buffish fringes) contrasting strongly with boldly barred brown/buff coverts. Underparts white.

IW   As *Ad WP* but some *Juv* inner medians retained, appearing lace-like through wear, but rest of coverts replaced by *Ad* type. In winter contrast in wear of worn inner medians and fresh outer coverts. Primaries slightly or moderately worn by winter. During January-May most birds either moult outer primaries (and inner secondaries, where the contrast of wear is very obvious) or have complete moult (but sometimes retaining some worn *Juv* secondaries). Those that have a complete moult are usually indistinguishable from *Ad*.

IS   Many cannot be told but those that moulted outers only show strong contrast between worn inners and fresh outers. A few summering in the south do not attain *SP*.

SEXING   ♀ averages larger (and heavier). In *SP* ♀ usually has bolder spotting than ♂ but great overlap and this is a difficult character.

BIOMETRICS

Wing	18 A♂	102-108	(105.6) :	15 J	99-113	(104.7)
	17 A♀	104-113	(109.0) :			
Bill	46 A	21-27	(24.1) :	15 J	22-26	(23.5)
Tarsus	46 A	21-25	(23.5) :	15 J	21-25	(22.9)
Tail	10 A♂	47-52	(49.2) :	10 J♂	46-51	(47.7)
	10 A♀	48-53	(51.1) :	10 J♀	44-52	(47.8)

REFERENCES   Ident. 8, 80B, Sex 55, Weight 86.

GREY-RUMPED SANDPIPER *Heteroscelus brevipes*

NC, NE and ME P. Long-distance migrant to W. Pacific coasts and islands.

IDENTIFICATION Like a medium to large *Tringa* but rather long-winged, long-tailed and short-legged. Whole upperparts grey, including wings and tail, but some narrow whitish fringing on rump and upper tail coverts. Flanks and underwing grey. Bill dusky becoming yellowish at base, legs yellowish. Very similar to *H. incanus*, from which by shorter deep section of nasal groove (ending at least 17 mm. from bill-tip), more extensive whitish fringing on rump and upper tail coverts, smaller size (wing mostly under 170 mm), and in *SP* by lighter barring underneath with more extensive clear white on belly and under tail coverts.

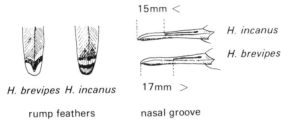

H. brevipes   H. incanus   H. incanus

                                     H. brevipes

H. brevipes H. incanus   17mm >

    rump feathers   nasal groove

AGEING see *H. incanus*

SEXING ♀ averages larger.

BIOMETRICS

Wing	18 A♂	158-170	(163.9) : 10 J♂	154-167	(161.6)
	16 A♀	160-175	(168.4) : 19 J♀	154-169	(162.5)
Bill	58 A	34-42	(37.7) : 48 J	35-42	(37.3)
Tarsus	63 A	29-34	(31.8) : 51 J	29-34	(31.4)

REFERENCES Moult 129.

WANDERING TATTLER *Heteroscelus incanus*

NW N. Long-distance migrant to Pacific coasts and islands.

IDENTIFICATION Very similar to *H. brevipes* (which see), but has longer nasal groove (extending to within 15mm. of bill tip), rump plain grey usually lacking whitish fringes, wing usually over 170mm., and heavier barring on underparts in *SP* extending to under tail coverts and leaving only a small area of belly unbarred.

AGEING (also for *H. brevipes*)

Ad SP Coverts grey with some narrow white fringes. Underparts white barred grey.

WP Upperparts grey; coverts grey with paler edges. Underparts white, with breast washed grey. Moult October-February, so primaries are slightly worn in autumn, and fresh in spring and summer.

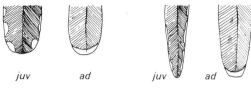

juv   ad   juv   ad

inner median coverts   tertials

Juv Upperparts and coverts greyish with extensive buffish-white fringes and dark subterminal bars; inner medians spotted buffish. Underparts white, with breast mottled greyish.

IW As *Ad WP* but coverts, especially inner medians, retain pale buff fringes and spots to winter. Primaries moderately worn in winter. Moult outer primaries January-August; a few have a complete moult. In late winter and spring most can be identified by contrast of new outer and old inner primaries. If have complete moult appear as *Ad*.

IS Some show contrast in primaries, with worn inners and fresh outers. Most remain in *WP*.

SEXING ♀ averages larger.

BIOMETRICS

Wing	13 A♂	163-186	(171.5)	:	8 J♂	163-182	(171.0)
	15 A♀	166-186	(175.9)	:	9 J♀	167-181	(171.9)
Bill	42 A	35-43	(39.1)	:	30J	37-43	(38.8)
Tarsus	45 A	30-35	(32.9)	:	31J	32-35	(33.4)

REFERENCES Moult 69, 129, Weight 70.

WILLET   *Catoptrophorus semipalmatus*

MC, ME and SE N. Short- to medium-distance migrant.

IDENTIFICATION Like an extra large *Tringa* or a smallish *Limosa*, with mainly pale grey plumage and a very striking wing-pattern. Blackish remiges have very bold white wingbar extending broadly to leading edge of primaries, and some inner secondaries are completely white. Axillaries and greater and median underwing coverts are black, lesser underwing coverts white, with white bases to remiges contrasting strongly underneath. Squarish white rump above pale grey tail. Bill straight, stoutish, almost black. Legs blue-grey.

AGEING

Ad SP Head, mantle and some coverts grey-brown mottled darker brown. Underparts white with breast spotted and flanks barred brown.

WP Upperparts uniform greyish; coverts when fresh have narrow white fringes. Underparts white with breast greyish. Moult August-November, so all primaries fresh in winter, slightly worn by summer. Primaries 1-4(5) with narrow white tips.

Juv Mantle, coverts and scapulars grey-brown with broad buff fringes and subterminal dark bars. Underparts white, greyish on breast.

| juv | ad | C.s. semipalmatus | C.s. inornatus |

inner median coverts   central tail feathers

IW As *Ad WP* but despite wear retained *Juv* coverts with buffish fringes and especially subterminal bars are clear to winter. *Ad* type coverts moulted in during late winter. Primaries 1-6 with extensive white tips, moderately worn by winter.

IS Very worn primaries, plumage generally pale.

SEXING ♀ averages larger, but there is geographical variation in size so care is needed.

GEOGRAPHICAL VARIATION Two races recognised. Nominate *semipalmatus* (E. USA) is smaller; in *SP* bars on underparts are much darker and more frequent and has strongly barred central tail feathers. *Inornatus* (C and W. USA) is larger, with relatively indistinct *SP*, and central tail feathers unbarred or only slightly barred. Many intermediates in plumage so care is needed. Size is useful (but not enough birds examined). Basic divisions are:—

	wing	*bill*	*tarsus*
semipalmatus	⩽ 205	⩽ 56	⩽ 60
inornatus	⩾ 210	⩾ 60	⩾ 64

BIOMETRICS very small sample of racially identified birds examined, so races are combined.

Wing	17 A♂	186-220	(202.6) : 37 J	184-222	(205.8)
	14 A♀	201-221	(211.0) :		
Bill	48 A	50-67	(59.1) : 37 J	54-65	(59.4)
Tarsus	48 A	50-70	(60.7) : 37 J	53-69	(62.0)

REFERENCES Biometrics, Moult 86.

TURNSTONE   *Arenaria interpres*

N H. Short- medium- or long-distance migrant.

IDENTIFICATION Smallish wader with short pointed dark bill (lower mandible angled up), and shortish orange legs. White lower back, upper tail coverts and base and tip to tail, blackish rump and broad nearly terminal tailband. Inner lessers and some outer scapulars white, clear white wingbar. From similar *A. melanocephala* by white on cheeks and throat and orange legs in all plumages, and by whitish crown and reddish-chestnut banding on mantle in *SP*. *See Plate 11.*

AGEING

Ad SP Extensive white on head and neck with blackish-brown streaking. Mantle, scapulars and tertials blackish-brown with extensive rufous-chestnut edges. Some coverts as scapulars, but others brownish with slightly paler edges. Legs bright orange.

WP Upperparts dark greyish-black/pale grey; coverts dark grey with paler edges. Moult in nominate *interpres* is late July-October but much later in south of range (October-February in S. Africa); in *morinella* October-February. Primaries fresh in winter and spring (most noticeably in *morinella*).

Juv As dull brown *Ad WP* but scapulars, tertials and coverts fringed pale chestnut-buff giving slightly scalloped impression. Legs dull yellowish-brown or orange.

IW As *Ad WP* but buff-fringed inner medians are retained to spring, although wear makes them difficult to see. Primaries slightly worn in midwinter, moderately worn by spring. In the south a few moult inner primaries and suspend in late winter.

IS Occasionally *Juv* inner medians retained, but best identified by very worn primaries. Moult is June-August, and *IS/2W* can be told until the outer primary is lost. Rarely attains full *SP* and many remain in *WP* south of breeding range. (Scandinavian birds more frequently return in *IS*.)

SEXING ♀ has larger wing on average. In *SP Ad* ♂ has cap white streaked black, nape mostly white, breast black, and mantle and coverts blackish with extensive deep chestnut fringes. *Ad* ♀ has cap whitish fairly extensively streaked brownish-black, nape buffish-white streaked brown, mantle with more limited area of dull red, coverts dark brown with some palish chestnut edges, and breast blackish with some light grey tips. *IS* birds attain partial *SP*, with ♂ almost as *Ad* ♀, but ♀ has very little *SP*.
Sexing is however difficult and safest with pairs on breeding grounds.

GEOGRAPHICAL VARIATION Two races recognized: nominate *interpres* (NE Canada, Greenland, Palaearctic) and *morinella* (rest of Nearctic), possibly with intermediates in Alaska. *Morinella* has shorter wing but only separable in *SP* when *morinella* has extensive brick-red/chestnut fringes on upperparts while *interpres* has paler (but still bright) chestnut fringes.

BIOMETRICS   *A.i. interpres*

Wing	23 A♂	147-163	(155.0) :	22 J♂	145-159	(153.1)
	13 A♀	150-164	(158.0) :	21 J♀	146-162	(153.2)
Bill	31 A♂	20-25	(22.0) :	11 J♂	19-23	(21.4)
	24 A♀	20-25	(22.0) :	17 J♀	20-24	(21.8)
Tarsus	30 A♂	25-27	(25.7) :	14 J♂	25-26	(25.4)
	22 A♀	24-27	(25.6) :	17 J♀	25-26	(25.5)

A.i. morinella

Wing	14 A♂	146-163	(152.6) :	22 J	141-158	(150.0)
	14 A♀	150-159	(154.1)			

REFERENCES   Moult 6, 120, Sex 95, Variation 52, Biometrics 44B, 94, 95, Weight 44B, 70, 92, 94, 95, 117, 149.

BLACK TURNSTONE   *Arenaria melanocephala*

NW N (W. and S. Alaska).   Short- to medium-distance migrant.

IDENTIFICATION   Size and shape as *A. interpres,* and similar white patterning on wings, back and tail, but much blacker above and on breast and always with throat and upper breast dark. Boldly black and white in *SP*. Bill blackish, legs dark purplish-brown.

AGEING

Ad SP   Head black with white spots on forehead, above lores. Breast black with extensive white spotting on sides extending onto neck. Mantle and coverts mainly black; belly white.

WP   Uniform brownish-black on head, breast and upperparts, with very small dull whitish patch near eye. Coverts uniform blackish, paling towards edge. Scapulars when fresh with narrow white edges; retained through winter, becoming worn in spring. Moult August-October, so primaries fresh in winter and slightly worn by spring.

Juv   Upperparts blackish-brown; mantle, coverts and scapulars with extensive pale buffish fringes. Breast brownish-grey.

IW   As *Ad WP* but buff fringes to inner medians may be retained to spring (but sometimes are lost by November). Primaries slightly worn in winter, moderately worn in spring.

IS   Very worn primaries; may attain *SP*.

SEXING   ♀ averages larger. In *SP* ♂ has more distinct head pattern, with larger white patch near eye.

159

Wing	8 A♂	148-156	(152.4)	:	5 J♂	147-150	(148.8)
	3 A♀	153-162	(157.0)	:	3 J♀	149-153	(151.7)
Bill	22 A	21-25	(23.2)	:	11 J	21-24	(21.8)
Tarsus	22 A	24-27	(25.5)	:	11 J	24-26	(25.3)

WILSON'S PHALAROPE   *Phalaropus tricolor*

MW and MC N. Long-distance migrant.

IDENTIFICATION   Smallish wader with lobed toes as other *Phalaropus*, but only phalarope with white rump and lacking wingbar. *SP* distinctive; in winter is very pale above. Bill very fine, black, longer than in *P. lobatus*. Legs longer than other phalaropes, usually black in *SP* and yellow in *WP* and juveniles. *See Plate 15.*

AGEING

Ad SP   (see sexing for details) at first partly obscured by whitish tips. Legs black.

WP   Upperparts including coverts uniform pale grey, although inner medians may have whitish fringe; underparts white. Legs yellow. Moult October-March, so primaries slightly worn in autumn, fresh in spring.

Juv   Upperparts and coverts brownish with extensive buff fringes. Underparts white, with sides of breast washed buff.

IW   As *Ad WP* but inner medians retain buff fringes to spring. Primaries fresh in autumn, slightly worn in winter and moderately worn by spring.

IS   Primaries very worn; many remain in *WP*.

SEXING   Dimorphic in size and *SP*.

In *SP*, *Ad* ♀ has cap and upper back blue-grey, black eye patch, bright chestnut-red sides of neck, and back grey and chestnut. *Ad* ♂ has cap and upper back brown sometimes tinged grey, eye patch dark brown, small chestnut area on side of neck, and back brown and chestnut.

At all times sexable on wing length. A♀ > 130, A♂ < 129, J♀ > 129, J♂ < 127. Bill and tarsus also longer in ♀ but with some overlap.

BIOMETRICS

Wing	32 A♂	119-129	(124.7)	:	7 J♂	116-126	(121.9)
	31 A♀	130-142	(135.4)	:	9 J♀	129-136	(132.0)
Bill	28 A♂	29-33	(31.0)	:	7 J♂	27-32	(29.6)
	29 A♀	31-36	(33.5)	:	7 J♀	32-36	(33.7)
Tarsus	32 A♂	29-34	(31.2)	:	9 J♂	29-32	(30.7)
	31 A♀	31-35	(32.8)	:	9 J♀	30-35	(32.4)

REFERENCES   General 61, Moult 13.

RED-NECKED PHALAROPE   *Phalaropus lobatus*

N H. Long-distance migrant wintering chiefly at sea in the tropics.

IDENTIFICATION   Small phalarope with white wingbar and sides to rump. Recalls small-medium calidrid but has needle-fine bill, distinctive *SP*, and blackish mark behind eye in *WP*. From *P. fulicarius* in *WP* by smaller size, finer bill, and darker grey mantle with white fringing and often some blackish feathers. Bill black, shorter than in *P. tricolor*. Legs slate-grey, paler or more yellowish in juvenile. *See Plate 15.*

AGEING

Ad SP (see sexing for details) when fresh partly obscured by whitish tips. Legs dark slate-grey.

WP   Mantle and coverts pale blue-grey (during autumn body moult mixed with a few brown feathers), with some whitish tips when fresh forming whitish lines. Blackish band on ear coverts. Few moulting birds examined, but apparently most moult from late autumn-winter; so by late winter primaries are fresh, and in summer are slightly worn. A few may moult July-September.

Juv   Cap brownish. Mantle dark brown with prominent golden-buff fringes to scapulars and tertials which form lines on back. Underparts whitish with pinkish-buff wash on throat. Legs yellowish-flesh to blueish-grey.

IW   Most of upperparts replaced by pale grey but some of dark cap is retained, also mantle is mottled blackish-brown and grey usually to spring. Golden-buff fringes on scapulars and tertials become pale yellow but are usually retained to spring. Primaries moderately worn by late winter. (Primary moult from January has been noted by Stresemann but we have no evidence of it on the few birds examined).

IS   Primaries very worn. Some attain partial *SP*.

SEXING   ♀ has longer wing on average. Separable in *SP*:-

Ad ♀ has crown, neck and back slate-grey, contrasting with clean white face and red neck patches which extend well into grey breastband.

Ad ♂ has crown, neck and back brown or brownish-grey; little red on neck and relatively indistinct whitish face; retain *SP* slightly later than ♀.

BIOMETRICS

Wing	51 A♂	103-114	(107.8)	: 19 J	102-113	(107.2)
	31 A♀	109-118	(113.4)	:		
Bill	17 A♂	19-22	(21.1)	: 15 J	19-23	(20.7)
	11 A♀	20-23	(21.6)	:		
Tarsus	18 A♂	19-22	(20.4)	: 11 J	19-22	(20.4)
	13 A♀	20-22	(20.8)	:		

REFERENCES General 61, Moult, Sex, Weight 58.

GREY PHALAROPE *Phalaropus fulicarius*

N H. Medium- to long-distance migrant wintering chiefly at sea.

IDENTIFICATION Largish phalarope with long wings and tail, shortish legs, and distinctive short broad bill. White wingbar and sides to rump, recalling *Calidris alba* in *WP* but with plain grey upperparts and flanks, blackish mask, and rather longer tail. *SP* distinctive. Mantle plainer than *P. lobatus* in *WP*, and always identified by size and bill. Bill yellow with black tip in *SP,* otherwise blackish usually with some yellowish at base. Legs brownish with yellowish lobes to toes, more greyish in *WP* and *Juv. See Plate 16.*

AGEING

Ad SP (see sexing for details) lost very quickly in August/mid-September. Bill yellow, tip black.

WP   Upperparts grey with darker shaft streaks; grey inner medians, tipped white. Some start moult near breeding grounds August-November, but others seem to moult at sea in winter.

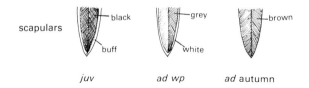

juv	*ad wp*	*ad* autumn

Juv   Upperparts rich dark brown and black with buff edges. Underparts white, with face, neck and upper breast washed pink-buff. Bill blackish, base tinged brown.

IW   Mantle and cap a mixture of grey *Ad* type and brown *Juv* feathers. Coverts, especially inner medians, retain buff·fringes to spring. Primaries appear moderately worn by spring.

IS   Only by very worn primaries. Often has some darkish back and rump feathers. 6 of 21♀ in *SP* had moulted outer primaries but no ♂ showed this (? *IS*).

162

SEXING   Dimorphic in *SP*. *Ad* ♂ has cap and mantle streaked sandy-brown and dark brown, cheeks with small area of buffish-white, and dull chestnut underparts, often with some white on belly. In *Ad* ♀ cap is very dark brown, mantle is blackish-brown with pale buff edgings, cheeks are white, and underparts are bright chestnut.

In *WP* and *Juv* size is helpful. For wing length: $Ad \leqslant 129$ ♂, $\geqslant 135$ ♀: *Juv* $\leqslant 127$ ♂, $\geqslant 132$♀. ♀ also has longer bill, but overlap is greater.

BIOMETRICS

Wing	51 A♂	122-134	(128.8) :	19 J♂	122-131	(125.7)
	30 A♀	130-141	(135.8) :	14 J♀	128-137	(133.1)
Bill	52 A♂	20-24	(22.1) :	20 J♂	20-22	(21.3)
	28 A♀	22-25	(23.2) :	19 J♀	21-25	(23.0)
Tarsus	16 A	20-23	(21.6) :	7 J	20-23	(21.3)

REFERENCES   General 61.

REFERENCES

SECTION A

General works and those referred to in the Introduction.

BENT, A. C. (1927, 1929). Life Histories of North American Shorebirds. *US. Natl. Mus. Bull.*, 142 and 146. Washington.

DEMENT'EV, G. P., GLADKOV, N. A. and SPANGENBERG, E. P. (1951). *Birds of the Soviet Union.* Vol. 3. Translation: Jersusalem 1969.

ETCHÉCOPAR, R. D. and HÜE, F. (1967). *The Birds of North Africa.* Edinburgh and London.

FALLA, R. A., SIBSON, R. B. and TURBOTT, E. G. (1970). *A Field Guide to the Birds of New Zealand.* London.

GLUTZ VON BLOTZHEIM, U. N., BAUER, K. M. and BEZZEL, E. (1975, 1977). *Handbuch der Vögel Mitteleuropas.* Vols. 6 and 7. Frankfurt am Main.

GODFREY, W. E. (1966). *The Birds of Canada.* Ottawa.

HARRISON, J. G. (1957). A review of skull pneumatisation in birds. *Bull. Brit. Orn. Club.* 77 : 70-77.

HARTERT, E. (1910-22). *Die Vögel der Palaarktischen Fauna.* (and Suppl. vols. 1923, 1932-36). Berlin.

HEINZEL, H., FITTER, R. and PARSLOW, J. (1972). *The Birds of Britain and Europe.* London.

HÜE, F. and ETCHÉCOPAR, R. D. (1970). *Les Oiseaux du Proche et du Moyen Orient.* Paris.

KING, B., WOODCOCK, M. and DICKINSON, E. C. (1975). *A Field Guide to the Birds of South-east Asia.* London.

KOSLOVA, E. V. (1961). *The Fauna of the USSR.* Nos. 80 and 81. Moscow.

McNEIL, R. and BURTON, J. (1972). Cranial pneumatisation patterns and Bursa Fabricius in North American shorebirds. *Wilson Bull.* 84 : 329-339.

MINTON, C. D. T. (1971). *Wader Ageing Guide.* Wader Study Group, Tring.

PALMER, R. S. (1968), in: *The Shorebirds of North America,* ed. G. D. Stout. New York.

PETERSON, R. T. (1947). *Field Guide to the Birds.* Boston.

PETERSON, R. T. (1961). *A Field Guide to Western Birds.* Boston.

PETERSON, R. T., MOUNTFORT, G. and HOLLOM, P. A. D. (1966). *A Field Guide to the Birds of Britain and Europe.* London.

PIENKOWSKI, M. W. (1976). Seasonal changes in bill lengths of Knots and a comment on bill measuring techniques for waders. *Wader Study Group Bull.* 17 : 12-14.

PIENKOWSKI, M. W. and MINTON, C. D. T. (1973). Wing length changes of the Knot with age and time since moult. *Bird Study* 20 : 63-68.

ROBBINS, C. S. (1973). Shorebird Identification. *East. Bird Band. Ass. News* 36 : 4-15.

ROBBINS, C. S., BRUUN, B. and ZIM, H. S. (1966). *Birds of North America.* New York.

SALIM ALI and RIPLEY, S. D. (1969). *Handbook of the Birds of India and Pakistan.* Vols. 2 and 3. Oxford.

SCHAUENSEE, R. M. de (1970). *A Guide to the Birds of South America.* Philadelphia.

SNOW, D. W. (1970). A Guide to moult in British birds. *BTO Guide,* no. 11. Tring.

SPENCER, R. (1976). *The Ringer's Manual.* BTO, Tring.

STRESEMANN, E. and V. (1966). Die Mauser der Vögel. *J. Orn.* 107, Sonderheft: 1-445 Berlin.

SVENSSON, L. (1975). *Identification Guide to European Passerines.* Stockholm.

VAURIE, C. (1965). *The Birds of the Palearctic Fauna. Non-Passeriformes.* London.

VOOUS, K. H. (1960). *Atlas of European Birds.* London.

VOOUS, K. H. (1973). List of Recent Holarctic bird species. Non-passerines. *Ibis* 115 : 612-638.

WITHERBY, H. F., JOURDAIN, F. C. R., TICEHURST, N. F. and TUCKER, B. W. (1940). *The Handbook of British Birds.* Vol. 4. London.

SECTION B

Selected references related to the species accounts.

1   ANDERSON, K. R. (1974). *Wader Study Group Bull.* 11 : 5-14.
2   ATKINSON, N., SUMMERS, R. and NICOLL, M. (1975). *Wader Study Group Bull.* 15 : 5-11.
3   BAKER, A. J. (1974). *N. Z. J. Mar. Freshwater Res.* 8 : 211-221.
4   BENGTSON, S-A. (1975). *Ibis* 117 : 100-102
5   BOERE, G. C. (1974). *Proc. IWRB Wader Symp. Warsaw 1973* : 83-98.
6   BOERE, G. C. (1977). *Ardea* in press.
7   BOERE, G. C., BRUIJNE, J. W. A. de and NIEBOER, E. (1973). *Limosa* 46 : 205-227.
8   BOERE, G. C. and ZEGERS, P. M. (1976). *Limosa* 49 : 12-16.
9   BRANSON, N. J. B. A. and MINTON, C. D. T. (1976). *Bird Study* 23 : 257-266.
10 BROWN, S. C. (1974). *Wader Study Group Bull.* 11 : 18-24.
11 BUB, H. (1958). *Beitr. z. Vogelkunde* 5 : 268-283.
12 BUB, H. and KOLAR-RLICKA, S. (1969). *Vogelwarte* 25 : 2-6.
13 BURGER, J. and HOWE, M. (1975). *Auk* 92 : 442-451.
14 BURTON, J. and McNEIL, R. (1976). *Bird-Banding* 47 : 201-209.
15 BYRKJEDAL, I. (1974). *Sterna* 13 : 1-14.
16 CARMICHAEL LOW, G. (1938). *Ibis* (14) 2 : 154-158.
17 CLAUSAGER, I. (1973). *Dan Rev. Game Biology*, vol. 8, no. 1.
18 CONOVER, B. (1943). *Condor* 45 : 226-228.
19 DARE, P. J. and MERCER, A. J. (1974a). *Bird Study* 21 : 180-184.
20 DARE, P. J. and MERCER, A. J. (1974b). *Ibis* 116 : 211-214.
21 DEMENT'EV, G. P. (1939). *Ibis* (14) 3 : 352-354.
22 DICK, W. J. A. (1976). *Rep. Oxf. & Camb. Maurit, Exped.* Cambridge.
23 DICK, W. J. A., PIENKOWSKI, M. W., WALTNER, M. and MINTON, C. D. T. (1976). *Ardea* 64 : 22-47.
24 EADES, R. A. and OKILL, J. D. (1976). *Ringing and Migration* 1 : 92-97.
25 EADES, R. A. and OKILL, J. D. (1977). *Bird Study* 24 : 62-63.
26 ELLIOTT, C. C. H., WALTNER, M., UNDERHILL, L. G., PRINGLE, J. G. and DICK, W. J. A. (1976). *Ostrich* 47 : 191-213.
27 ETHERIDGE, B. (1971). *Wader Study Group Bull.* 3 : 5-7.
28 EVANS, P. R. (1964). *Bird Study* 11 : 23-38.
29 EVANS, P. R. (1975). *Emu* 75 : 227-229.
30 EVANS, P. R. and SMITH, P. C. (1975). *Wildfowl* 26 : 64-76.
31 FLETCHER, M. (1976). *Wader Study Group Bull.* 18 : 5-6.
32 FOLKESTAD, A. O. (1974). *Wader Study Group Bull.* 13 : 9-10.
33 FOURNIER, O. (1969). *Nos Oiseaux* 30 : 87-102.
34 FOURNIER, O. and D'ELBEE, E. (1974). *Bull. L'Office Nat. Chasse* : 183-189.
35 FOURNIER, O. and SPITZ, F. (1969a). *L'Oiseau et R.F.O.* 39 : 15-20.
36 FOURNIER, O. and SPITZ, F. (1969b). *L'Oiseau et R.F.O.* 39 : 242-251.
37 FOURNIER, O. and SPITZ, F. (1970). *L'Oiseau et R.F.O.* 40 : 69-81.
38 FRY, C. H., ASH, J. S. and FERGUSON-LEES, I. J. (1970). *Ibis* 112 : 58-82.
39 FUCHS, E. (1973). *Orn. Beob.* 70 : 113-134.
40 GIBSON, F. (1971). *Condor* 73 : 444-454.
41 GLUTZ VON BLOTZHEIM, U. (1972). *J. Orn.* 113 : 323-333.
42 GOODYER, L. R. (1976). *Wader Study Group Bull.* 18 : 9-12.
43 GRAUL, W. D. (1975). *Wilson Bull.* 87 : 6-31.
44A GREEN, G. H. (1973). *Wader Study Group Bull.* 8 : 4-9.
44B GREEN, G. H. and GREENWOOD, J. J. D. (1977). *Rep. Exped. NE Greenland 1972.* Dundee Univ.
45 GRIEVE, A. (1972). *Morecambe Bay Wader R. G. Rep.*, no. 2.
46 HALE, W. G. (1971). *Z. Jour. Linn. Soc.* 50 : 199-268.
47 HALE, W. G. (1973). *Z. Jour. Linn. Soc.* 53 : 177-236.

48   HAMILTON, R. B. (1975). *A. O. U. Ornith, Monogr.*, no. 17.
49   HARRIS, M. P. (1967). *Ibis* 109 : 180-193.
50   HARRISON, J. M. and HARRISON, J. G. (1965). *Brit. Birds* 58 : 10-14.
51   HARRISON, J. M. and HARRISON, J. G. (1967). *Bull. Brit. Orn. Club* 87 : 142-148.
52   HARRISON, J. M. and HARRISON, J. G. (1971). *Bull. Brit. Orn. Club* 91 : 167-171.
53   HAVERSCHMIDT, F. (1963). *The Black-tailed Godwit.* Leiden.
54   HAYMAN, P. J. (1956). *Brit. Birds* 49 : 312-313.
55   HAYS, H. (1972). *Living Bird* 11 : 43-57.
56   HEPPLESTON, P. B. and KERRIDGE, D. F. (1970). *Bird Study* 17 : 48-49.
57   HILDÉN, O. (1975). *Ornis Fennica* 52 : 117-146.
58   HILDÉN, O. and VUOLANTO, S. (1972). *Ornis Fennica* 49 : 57-85.
59   HOBSON, W. (1972). *Proc. Western Found. Vert. Zool.* 2 (1) : 5-26.
60   HOFFMAN, L. (1957). *Alauda* 25 : 30-42.
61   HOHN, E. O. (1965). *Die Wassertreter.* Neue Brehm-Bucherei, Wittemberg.
62   HOLMES, R. T. (1966). *Condor* 68 : 3-46.
63   HOLMES, R. T. (1971). *Condor* 73 : 93-99.
64   HOLMES, R. T. (1972). *Am. Midland Nat.* 87 : 472-491.
65   HUSSELL, D. J. T. and PAGE. G. W. (1976). *Wilson Bull.* 88 : 632-653.
66   JEHL, J. R. (1970). *Evolution* 24 : 311-319.
67   JEHL, J. R. (1973). *Wilson Bull.* 85 : 115-147.
68   JOHNSON, D. W. and MACFARLANE, R. W. (1967). *Condor* 69 : 156-168.
69   JOHNSON, O. W. (1977). *Auk* 94 : 222-230.
70   JOHNSON, O. W. and MORTON, M. L. (1976). *Condor* 78 : 144-145.
71   KENNEDY, R. J. (1973). *Wader Study Group Bull.* 9 : 4-7.
72   KIRCHNER, K. (1969). *Die Uferschnepfe (Limosa limosa)* Neue Brehm-Bucherei No. 413, Wittemberg.
73   KITTLE, T. (1975). *Ringing and Migration* 1 : 52-55.
74   KLIEBE, K. (1971). *Vogelring* 33 : 63-67.
75   KLOMP, H. (1946). *Limosa* 19 : 76-117.
76   KOSLOVA, E. V. (1957). *Proc. 2nd Baltic Ornith. Conf.* : 153-158.
77   LILJA, I. (1968). *Porrin Lintutietellinen Yhdistys* : 40-43.
78   LOVENSKIÖLD, H. L. (1950). *Dansk Orn. Foren. Tidsskr.* 44 : 161-167.
79   MACLEAN, S. F. and HOLMES, R. T. (1971). *Auk* 88 : 893-901.
80A MADGE, S. C. (1977). *Brit. Birds* 70 : 146-152.
80B MADGE, S. C. (1977). *Brit. Birds* 70 : 346-348.
81   MARTIN, F. W. (1964). *J. Wildl. Mgmt.* 28 : 287-293.
82   MARTIN-LOF, P. (1958). *Vär Fagelvärld* 17 : 287-301.
83   MASCHER, J. W. (1966). *Bird Banding* 37 : 1-34.
84   MASCHER, J. W. and MARSCTROM, V. (1976). *Ornis Scand* 7 : 49-59.
85   McNEIL, R. (1969). *Can. J. Zool.* 47 : 525-536.
86   McNEIL, R. (1970). *L'Oiseau et R.F.O.* 40 : 185-302.
87   McNEIL, R. (1971). *Condor* 73 : 472-475.
88   McNEIL, R. and BURTON, J. (1973). *Carib. J. Sci.* 13 : 257-278.
89   McNEIL, R. and CADIEUX, F. (1972). *Nat. Canadien* 99 : 589-606.
90   MERCER, A. J. (1968). *Bird Study* 15 : 93-98.
91   MIDDLEMISS, E. (1961). *Ostrich* 32 : 107-121.
92   MINTON, C. D. T. (1975). *Wash Wader Ringing Group Rep.* 1973/74.
93   MINTON, C. D. T. and STANLEY, P. I. (1972). *Wader Study Group Bull.* 6 : 7-10.
94   MORRISON, R. I. G. (ed.) (1972). *Rep. Cambridge-Iceland Exped.*
95   MORRISON, R. I. G. (1975). *Bird-Banding* 46 : 290-301.
96   MORRISON, R. I. G. (1976). *Ibis* 118 : 237-246.
97A MORRISON, R. I. G., PIENKOWSKI, M. W., and STANLEY, P. I. (1971). *Rep. Cambridge/Lond. Iceland Exped.*
97B MURRAY, B. G. and JEHL, J. R. (1964). *Bird-Banding* 35 : 253-263.
98   NETHERSOLE-THOMPSON, D. (1957). *The Greenshank.* London.
99   NETHERSOLE-THOMPSON, D. (1973). *The Dotterel.* London.

100 NIEBOER, E. (1972). *Ardea* 60 : 112-119.
101 NISBET, I. C. T. (1961). *Brit. Birds* 54 : 343-356.
102 O. A. G. MUNSTER (1975). *J. Orn.* 116 : 455-488.
103 O. A. G. MUNSTER (1976). *Vogelwarte* 28 : 278-293.
104 OUELLET, H., McNEIL, R. and BURTON, J. (1973). *Can. Field Nat.* 87 : 291-300.
105 OWEN, R. B. and KROHN, W. B. (1973). *Wilson Bull.* 85 : 31-41.
106 PAGE, G. (1974a). *Bird-Banding* 45 : 93-105.
107 PAGE, G. (1974b). *Western Birds* 5 : 1-12.
108 PAGE, G. and FEARIS, B. (1971). *Bird-Banding* 42 : 297-298.
109 PAGE, G., FEARIS, B. and JUREK, R. M. (1972). *Calif. Birds* 3 : 79-86.
110 PAGE, G. and MIDDLETON, A. L. A. (1972). *Bird-Banding* 43 : 85-96.
111 PEARSON, D. (1972). *Wader Study Group Bull.* 7 : 14-15.
112 PEARSON, D. (1974). *Wader Study Group Bull.* 12 : 6-12.
113 PEARSON, D., PHILLIPS, J. H. and BACKHURST, G. C. (1970). *Ibis* 112 : 199-208.
114 PFISTER, H. (1972). *Safring News* 1 (1) : 26.
115 PHILLIPS, A. R. (1975). *American Birds* 29 : 799-806.
116 PIENKOWSKI, M. W. (ed.) (1972). *Rep. Univ. East Angl. Moroc. 1971 Exped.*
117 PIENKOWSKI, M. W. (ed.) (1975). *Rep. Studies Coast. Birds Moroc. 1972.* Norwich.
118 PIENKOWSKI, M. W. and DICK, W. J. A. (1975). *Ornis Scand.* 6 : 151-167.
119 PIENKOWSKI, M. W. and KNIGHT, P. J. (1974). *Ibis* 117 : 114.
120 PIENKOWSKI, M. W., KNIGHT, P. J., STANYARD, D. J. and ARGYLE, F. B. (1976). *Ibis* 118 : 347-365.
121 PIENKOWSKI, M. W. and MINTON, C. D. T. (1973). *Bird Study* 20 : 63-68.
122 PITELKA, F. A. (1950). *Univ. Calif. Publ. Zool.* 50 : 1-108.
123 PORTENKO, L. A. (1936). *Auk* 53 : 194-197.
124 PORTENKO, L. A. (1957). *J. Orn.* 98 : 454-466.
125 PORTENKO, L. A. (1959). *J. Orn.* 100 : 141-172.
126 POSLAWSKI, A. N. (1969). *Falke* 16 : 184-188.
127 PRATER, A. J. (1975). *Ringing and Migration* 1 : 43-47.
128 PRATER, A. J. and WILSON, J. (1972). *Wader Study Group Bull.* 5 : 9-13.
129 PRATER, A. J. and MARCHANT, J. H. (1975). *Bull. Brit. Orn. Club* 95 : 120-122.
130 REYNOLDS, C. M. (1976). *Wader Study Group Bull.* 19 : 10-12.
131 RITTINGHAUS, H. (1956). *J. Orn.* 97 : 117-155.
132 ROWAN, W. (1932). *Auk* 49 : 14-35.
133 SALOMONSEN, F. (1947). *Dansk Orn. Foren. Tidsskr.* 41 : 143-145.
134 SCHMITT, M. B. (1974). *Safring News* 3 (1) : 29.
135 SCHMITT, M. B. and WHITEHOUSE, P. J. (1976). *Ostrich* 47 : 179-190.
136 SHELDON, W. G. (1962). *The Book of the American Woodcock.* Amherst.
137A SHORTEN, M. (1974). *Game Conservancy Rep.*, no. 21.
137B SMITH, N. G. (1969). *Ibis* 111 : 177-188.
138 SOIKKELI, M. (1966). *Bird Study* 13 : 256-269.
139 SOIKKELI, M. (1974). *Bird Study* 21 : 151-154.
140 SPAANS, A. L. (1976). *Bird-Banding* 47 : 359-364.
141 STANLEY, P. I. and MINTON, C. D. T. (1972). *Brit. Birds* 65 : 365-380.
142 STERBETZ, I. (1974). *Die Brachschwalbe* Neue Brehm-Bucherei no. 462, Wittemburg.
143A SUMMERS, R. W. (1976). *Safring News* 5 (1) : 17-18.
143B SUMMERS, R. W. and COOPER, J. (1977). *Ostrich* 48 : 28-40.
144 TAYLOR, R. C. (1974). *Wader Study Group Bull.* 11 : 15-17.
145 THOMAS, D. G. and DARTNALL, A. J. (1970a). *Emu* 70 : 87.
146 THOMAS, D. G. and DARTNALL, A. J. (1970b). *Emu* 70 : 89.
147 THOMAS, D. G. and DARTNALL, A. J. (1971a). *Emu* 71 : 49-53.
148 THOMAS, D. G. and DARTNALL, A. J. (1971b). *Emu* 71 : 153-158.
149 THOMPSON, M. C. (1973). *Living Bird* 12 : 5-23.
150 TREE, A. J. (1971). *Wader Study Group Bull.* 4 : 6.
151 TREE, A. J. (1973). *Safring News* 2 (2) : 23-25.
152 TREE, A. J. (1974a). *Safring News* 3 (2) : 31-33.

153 TREE, A. J. (1974b). *Safring News* 3 (3) : 21-24.
154 TUCK, L. (1972). *The Snipes.* Ottawa.
155 USPENSKI, S. M. (1969). *Die Strandläufer Eurasieus* (Gattung *Calidris*) Neue Brehm-Bucherei no. 420, Wittemburg.
156 VÄISÄNEN, R. A. (1969). *Ann. Acad. Sci. Fenn.* Ser. A. IV, no. 149.
157 VAURIE, C. (1963). *Amer. Mus. Novit.* no. 2131.
158 VERNON, J. D. R. (1963). *Brit. Birds* 56 : 233-237.
159 VIELLIARD, J. (1971). Thesis, Ecole Norm. Superieure. Paris.
160 VIELLIARD, J. (1972). *Alauda* 40 : 321-342.
161 WALLACE, D. I. M. (1974). *Brit. Birds* 67 : 1-16.
162 WALLACE, D. I. M. (1976). *Brit. Birds* 69 : 377-383.
163 WALMSLEY, J. G. (1976). *Alauda* 44 : 334-335.
164 WALTNER, M. (1976). *Safring News* 5 (2) : 14-16.
165 WEBSTER, J. D. (1942). *Condor* 44 : 205-211.
166 WHITE, E. and GITTINS, J. C. (1964). *Bird Study* 11 : 257-261.
167 WILLIAMSON, K. and RUTTLEDGE, R. F. (1957). *Brit. Birds* 50 : 524-526.
168 WYNNE-EDWARDS, V. C. (1957). *Scot. Nat.* 69 : 89-93.